STO

7·24·79

7·24·79

THE QUICK KNIFE

UNNECESSARY SURGERY U.S.A.

DUANE F. STROMAN

National University Publications
KENNIKAT PRESS // 1979
Port Washington, N.Y. // London

Manufactured in the United States of America

Published by
Kennikat Press Corp.
Port Washington, N. Y./London

Library of Congress Cataloging in Publication Data

Stroman, Duane F
    The Quick Knife

    (National university publications)
    Includes index.
    1. Surgery, Unnecessary—U.S.
I. Title [DNLM: 1. Malpractice. 2. Surgery.
WO 34 S921Q]
RD27.8.S87   362.1'97'0973   78-31791
ISBN 0-8046-9226-2

CONTENTS

2060138

PREFACE

When I first heard the term "unnecessary surgery" and read brief reports of it nearly two decades ago, I felt a moral repulsion. I thought, how hideous to subject a person to pain and suffering while extracting money from him; and doing it under the guise of caring for him and curing him.

At that time I could not find any cases of physicians who had been tried as criminals for subjecting patients to needless surgery. My first response, since I was trained as a sociologist, was to believe that this special treatment of physicians was due to our class-oriented system of justice. As I recall, my reasoning at that time went something like this: If a nonsurgeon were to cut open a person, remove a healthy organ, and simultaneously rob the person of $500, the police would charge him with felonious assault and battery, robbery, and probably other offenses. And if the doctor said he did it to help the victim, we would call him psychotic—out of touch with reality—and have him examined by psychiatrists to determine if he were criminally insane.

Since that early reaction, and with extensive reading on the subject in the meantime, my opinion has been greatly modified. But there is an element of truth in my first reaction. There is a class-biased system of justice which does exist and which gives special treatment to fraudulent doctors. At least a few physician surgeons have performed unnecessary surgery simply for the fee where there was no medical justification for it.

If a surgeon does this most blatant type of unnecessary and unjustified surgery, the chances are that it will not be detected unless he does it systematically and uncleverly. And should he be detected, he may only have his wrists slapped by a hospital peer review comittee that will tell him to shape up. Or he may lose his privileges at one hospital; but this won't keep him from moving to another community or state to pursue a deviant practice again. Or a little worse, he may have his practice and reputation hurt if a malpractice suit, particularly a successful one for the patient, is brought against him. But if he has sufficient malpractice coverage, the suit may not hurt him financially. Patients indirectly pay for malpractice insurance through higher fees and hospital charges. At worst, he may lose his license to practice; and in medical circles, losing one's license may be nearly as bad as imprisoning a doctor, maybe worse.

But my ideas on what is unnecessary surgery have been modified most. I have come to realize, as I will describe more fully in chapter 3, that unnecessary and necessary surgery are neither black and white nor exhaustive categories. Rather, in their purest forms they are two points at the opposite ends of a continuum marked by many shades of gray in between.

At one end of the continuum will be surgery that is both unnecessary and unjustifiable. Some of it is fraudulent—undertaken to serve the economic motives of doctors. Some of it is due to the poor diagnostic skill of the surgeon. But as we shall see, this makes the evaluation of intent of the doctor very difficult.

At the other end of the continuum will be surgery that is necessary and justifiable either to save a person's life or to prevent harm and suffering. But on this long continuum will be many shades of medical and lay opinion. As we shall see, some unnecessary surgery may be justifiable, some of it not. And what may be seen as desirable or borderline by one physician or patient may be seen in a different way by another doctor or patient.

There are differences of opinion in many areas of medicine. This is so for several reasons. Some doctors and surgeons have had different experiences or results with the use of the same surgical procedure. This may be due to a variety of factors such as surgical skills, medical management, their training, and perhaps even their charismatic effect on patients. And patients presenting symptoms are unique both physiologically and psychologically. In many areas of medicine, including the efficacy and utility of some surgical procedures, sound scientific data is not yet available. Take coronary bypass surgery for example. It may be another three to five years before physicians have very sound data on what types this procedure helps, in what ways it helps them, and how much it helps them. Meanwhile it could be an expensive fad operation for some patients—like a number of other surgical procedures which were used for a period of time and then discarded. Or it may help some patients by relieving them of angina, preventing heart attacks, or prolonging life. But it will take years really to find out as data slowly accumulate on thousands who had or did not have the surgery and how they fared with and without it.

All this is to say that in many areas and in a number of ways medicine is an art. When some of the unknowns are discovered, it should become more of a science.

Furthermore, I have also modified my opinion as to the reasons that there is unnecessary surgery. My early understanding of it led me to believe it was simply due to the economic motivations of surgeons, of whom we have a surplus. That still is a factor and an important one. But there are other reasons too, some of them woven into complex inducements to surgery.

There are, as we shall see later in more detail, fad operations; some tonsillectomies and hysterectomies, for example, fit into this category. Between 1970 and 1975 the number of hysterectomies jumped 27 percent in this country. The highest hysterectomy rate in the world is not due to more sickness among American women, but to the fact that many women want the operation and many obstetricians and gynecologists go along with them if they do not actually promote it. While some doctors do this procedure only in cases of cancer, others undertake it as a method of birth control, or to eliminate the risk of cancer; still others perform it to free women of their menstrual bleeding and cramps.

Some unnecessary surgery is due to poor diagnostic skills; one surgeon believes surgery is called for with certain symptoms when many surgeons would say it is not. And some questionable surgery comes from a medicalized cultural climate in which new and innovative surgical procedures provide *hope*—hope for greater beauty as in cosmetic surgery, or hope for greater mobility with prosthetic hip and knee joints, or hope for greater longevity and less pain with coronary bypass surgery.

That what is necessary surgery is a controversial area was pointed out several years ago when a government subcommittee released a report on its dimensions. In January of 1976 the House Subcommittee on Oversight and Investigations of the Committee on Interstate and Foreign Commerce released a report entitled "Cost and Quality of Health Care:

Unnecessary Surgery." It estimated "2.38 million surgical procedures were unnecessarily performed in 1974 at a cost to the American public of $3.92 billion." It also estimated that these unnecessary surgeries led to 11,900 deaths. Some have made higher estimates. Ralph Nader estimated there were at least 3.2 million unnecessary operations annually, which resulted in about 16,000 deaths. When Dr. Edgar Berman was asked if he agreed with this estimate, he responded: "Let's cut it in half. Let's say it's a million and a half unnecessary operations. That's a hell of a lot. There are a certain number of unnecessary procedures done because of an honest mistake. But the other unnecessary operations are done for the obvious reason—money."

While some doctors accepted these statistics, or did not publicly offer refutation of them, the American Medical Association denounced the government report. Dr. James Sammons, executive vice president of the AMA, wrote a letter to the subcommittee chairman, John Moss, charging the report was unsound, unscientific, contained errors in data, and so on. While we will elaborate on this controversy in chapter 1, it is sufficient to say here that the report raised some very important issues about the quality of American surgical care, the cost of it, the effects of the fee system on the amount of it, and how medical care is regulated in the United States. These are some of the major issues I want to explore in this book.

Because surgery varies tremendously in scope, complexity, and purpose, we will explore the meaning of unnecessary surgery in a number of contexts from "emergency" appendectomies to cosmetic surgery to disguise an "ethnic" nose or tighten wrinkled skin. As we do so, we shall really be exploring basic values of the good, the beautiful, and the helpful. Greed, vanity, and psychological problems often crop up beside altruism to relieve pain and extend life in the performance of surgery—and among both patients and surgeons.

The exploration of what is unnecessary surgery also raises other value questions of a complex nature. When medical education was paid for by the person getting it or when medical care was paid for by the individual out of his own pocket, the role of public bodies in such decisions was much more distant. But now that federal and state governments and a variety of quasi-public bodies such as health insurers are involved in paying for the staggering costs of medical care, they are becoming increasingly concerned with how their money is spent. Who is going to see that public money is spent for necessary and important surgery and hospitalization?

Fortunately or unfortunately, the decision to operate is no longer solely the concern of the patient and his surgeon. Nor is the decision to educate more surgeons than we need.

In writing about unnecessary surgery, I might add, I have no personal axe to grind. I have had one operation in my life; it was to remove a torn cartilage in my knee due to a football injury in high school. It was before I ever heard the term "unnecessary surgery." In retrospect and by some standards it could be considered unnecessary surgery. I could have learned to live with the pain, swelling, and stiffness in my knee that I experienced following any strenuous exercise. I could have modified my lifestyle. But I considered it then and now justifiable in terms of what is important to me.

And, I might add, I believe that most surgical procedures in the United States are necessary and well done. American surgical care has been innovative and for the most part is a world leader. A book could easily be written about that aspect of American medicine. But I have chosen to write about a problem in American surgical care—unnecessary surgery. Along the way I shall also be looking at some other problems, including poor surgical care, which is also expensive in terms of patient suffering, mortality, and financial cost.

I would like to thank Mary Jane Brown for translating scrawled pages into legible type. I wish to thank the Juniata College administration for providing typing and telephone services to me. I wish to thank a number of physicians whose comments were most helpful but who shall remain anonymous. And last, I should apologize to my wife June and children Steven, Susan, Karen, and David, for my frequent absence from home during the time I was writing this book.

THE QUICK KNIFE

ABOUT THE AUTHOR

Dr. Duane F. Stroman is Professor of Sociology at Juniata College in Huntingdon, Pennsylvania. His research projects and monographs have included a study of drug use among high school students and the transportation problems of the elderly in rural areas. Duane Stroman is the author of *The Medical Establishment and Social Responsibility* (Kennikat Press, 1976).

1

TOO MUCH SURGERY—WHO SAYS?

The Subcommittee estimates that 2.38 million surgical procedures were unnecessarily performed in 1974 at a cost to the American public of $3.92 billion. . . . It is estimated that unnecessary surgeries led to 11,900 deaths last year.

We conclude that far too many physicians perform surgical operations and that work loads of surgical specialists are modest. [Rita Nickerson and four other scientists]

Approximately 24 percent of all procedures recommended were not confirmed [in their study] [Dr. Eugene G. McCarthy and Geraldine Widmer]

The greatest single curse in medicine is the curse of unnecessary operations, and there would be fewer of them, if the doctor got the same salary whether he operated or not. [Dr. Richard Cabot, professor of medicine at Harvard, 1938]

Unnecessary surgery is a standard procedure. . . . Nontechnical functions prevail in the removal of adenoids: more than 90 percent of all tonsillectomies performed in the United States are technically unnecessary, yet 20 to 30 percent of all children still undergo the operation. One in a thousand dies directly as a consequence of the operation and 16 in a thousand suffer from serious complications. All lose valuable immunity mechanisms. All are subject to emotional aggression: they are incarcerated in a hospital, separated from their parents, and introduced to the unjustified and more often than not pompous cruelty of the medical establishment. [Ivan Illich]

Surgery is big business in the United States. In 1973 over 13 million people underwent operations in short-term-stay, nonfederal hospitals.

This is expected to increase to about 19 million operations by 1978. About 70 percent of these people had one operation in the year, 22 percent two operations, and 8 percent three or more operations. In addition, some operations were done in federal hospitals as well as physicians' offices. This means that about one out of thirteen people are operated on annually. They account for about 41 percent of hospital discharges and a sizable but smaller percentage of a number of visits to physicians' offices. Because nearly one-third of all doctors perform some surgery and about 69,000 doctors consider it their specialty, it is a multi-billion-dollar business. Furthermore, it is responsible for the employment of millions of others in hospital supply firms and in hospitals, who assist in diagnosis, anesthesiology, operating rooms, and post-operative care.

Because surgery is such an important part of a medical care system under fire for over a decade now, the discussion of unnecessary surgery is a hot topic. The central questions I want to explore are the meanings and definitions of unnecessary surgery, the extent of it, its effects, the reasons for its occurrence, and what can be done about it. Along the way I shall explore a number of interesting topics: the quality of United States surgical care, the nature of the doctor-patient relationship, and changing patterns of surgery such as the rapid rise in plastic and heart surgery and the decrease in tonsillectomies which reflect changes in consumer demand, surgical technology, and surgical judgment. I shall also explore how surgery is used as a placebo, the supply and control of surgery and surgeons, and some fee-related practices such as highly variable fees and fee splitting. Finally, we shall need to look at our system of medical care, centered as it is around fee practice, and the meaning of the right to medical care. As government is increasingly becoming involved in ensuring that right, legislators and citizens are finding that it is terribly expensive. One must raise the question as to whether private and public funds are well spent.

In the 1950s, 1960s, and 1970s a number of studies indicated there was some unnecessary surgery going on—surgery that apparently was not medically needed but was helping doctors financially. Most of it may be attributable to poor diagnostic judgment, the uncertainty of much diagnosis, the pecuniary motivations of doctors, and the growing surplus of surgeons. In chapters 5, 6, and 7 I shall look at this evidence in detail. One report found that for its population the United States had twice as many surgeons and twice the amount of surgery as Great Britain. Other

studies showed that when medical records were reviewed after operations, considerable evidence was found that cast doubt on much of the
elective and even some of the emergency surgery. Other studies found
that the amount of surgery varied according to the availability of surgeons
and the number of beds available in which to place patients. And several
"second opinion" studies, where a second doctor, a surgeon, advised
on the need for surgery, found about one out of five recommended operations that did not need to be performed. Furthermore, in contrasting the
number of operations performed and patient hospital days involved in
surgical care provided by salaried physicians in comparison to fee-for-
service doctors, a number of studies showed that fewer beds were needed
and less surgery was performed by salaried doctors than by fee doctors.
This is highly suggestive of one of the roots of what are sometimes called
remunerectomies.

After the 1965 passage of Medicare and the new Medicaid legislation
to provide medical care for the elderly and indigent, the amount of
research and concern about overutilization of all medical services,
including surgery, began to rise. Now that government was paying for a
growing proportion of medical services in a highly inflationary sector of
the economy, it was concerned with whether federal funds were being
wisely spent. Investigations revealed extensive fraud in the Medicare and
Medicaid programs. As part of an investigatory process, the House Subcommittee on Oversight and Investigations of the Committee on Interstate
and Foreign Commerce held hearings on unnecessary surgery beginning in
1974.

From the beginning the hearings aroused concern, considerable
publicity, and strong stands by representatives, physicians, and patients.
When the final report was issued in January of 1976 under the title "Cost
and Quality of Health Care: Unnecessary Surgery," the American Medical
Association responded. In early February Dr. James Sammons, executive
vice president of the AMA, wrote a letter to Representative John E. Moss,
a Democrat from California, who headed the unnecessary surgery subcommittee. In his letter he called the report a "monumental deceit on the
public." The government report had estimated there were 2.38 million
unnecessary operations in 1974 and that the hospital and surgical costs
for them was $3.92 billion. Sammons wrote, "We reject the notion that
Americans have been subjected to millions of unnecessary operations
that have wasted billions of dollars and cost thousands of lives." He also
lambasted the quality of the report: "The report is unsound in concept,

unscientific in method, contains errors in data and information, distorts the testimony presented to the subcommittee and bases its main conclusions on an incomplete and improperly defined study." Sammons said it was slanderous to surgeons to imply that some would operate "solely for personal gain." He called the report "nothing more nor less than a dishonest piece of political propaganda." Representative Moss responded by saying the letter was "highly offensive and unfair." On May 11 the AMA called for new hearings on unnecessary surgery, saying the Moss study was biased and inaccurate.

How did the House subcommittee arrive at the estimates of 2.38 million unnecessary operations, with a cost of $3.92 billion and 11,900 lives? Was the report biased?

The figure of 2.38 million unnecessary operations came by an indirect route. First the subcommittee got several estimates of the amount of surgery in the United States. These estimates ranged from 18.4 million procedures to 15.96 million procedures. However, since some unknown amount—maybe 20 percent—of these were not elective procedures, and since some patients have more than one operation in a hospital, partly because some diagnostic tests involve surgery, they felt that 14 million patients undergoing surgery in 1974 was a "reasonable estimate."

Next they made an estimate about the amount of unnecessary surgery performed. Here they turned to Dr. Eugene G. McCarthy for advice. He reported on a presurgical screening program he headed that had functioned in a New York union. In this program, all persons who had surgery recommended to them by a doctor were requested to get a second opinion about the need for it prior to admission for in-hospital elective surgery. Eighty-four percent of the union members or their dependents did get a second opinion before undertaking surgery. In 17 percent of these cases the need for surgery was not confirmed. Multiplying the national figure of 14 million surgical procedures by 17 percent "unconfirmed" resulted in an estimate of 2.38 million unnecessary operations. However, in his original study about nonconfirmed elective procedures, Dr. McCarthy said that "the findings presented here cannot be applied to the general population undergoing elective operations." He also wrote, "The findings of this report should be considered preliminary." This was so, he argued, because some of the patients who did not immediately have surgery as a result of the second opinion might need it later, or some other medical treatment might be needed.

The subcommittee also relied on Dr. McCarthy for helping to estimate cost. He found that daily hospital bed charges in New York City at the time were about $141, which was then multiplied by the average length of stay of 7.3 days for the "nine most frequently unconfirmed diagnoses." To this resulting figure of $1,029 were added $500 for the surgeon and $125 for the anesthesiologist. The subcommittee took this figure, $1,654, rounded it off to $1,650, and multiplied it by 2.38 million unnecessary surgeries to come up with the $3.92 billion national estimate.

Using the same assumptions and figures, the subcommittee estimated that $816 million of federal money was spent on unnecessary surgery for Medicare patients and $272 million for Medicaid patients. The sub-committee concluded, "To the extent that HEW has failed to implement cost control procedures mandated by Congress, it can be said that HEW is responsible for *waste* of more than $1 billion."

The subcommittee came up with what it considered a low estimate of the number of people who died as a result of unnecessary surgery— 11,900. It received different estimates based primarily on varying esti-mates of what percent of people are discharged dead from hospitals following surgery. For example, Dr. Sidney Wolfe, director of the Public Citizens Health Research Group, estimated that a .5 percent mortality rate on 3.2 million unnecessary medical procedures would result in 16,000 deaths annually. However, HEW's Office of Research and Statistics found that 5.2 percent of Medicare patients discharged from hospitals in 1967 were discharged dead following surgery: 1,609,539 discharges, 85,222 dead. But most of these were elderly people, for whom the mortality rate following surgery may be four to six times higher than for the whole population.

Dr. Virgil Slee, president of the Commission on Professional and Hospital Activities, said that of 7,600,000 patients operated on during the first six months of 1975, 105,000 were discharged dead, yielding a mortality rate of 1.4 percent for all surgery. However, the mortality rate for elective surgery is lower, especially for tonsillectomies and abdominal hysterectomies. Consequently the committee used a .5 percent mortality rate on 2.38 million procedures to come up with the figure of 11,900 dead as a result of unnecessary surgery.

These numbers are significant. If they are at all accurate, they reflect a lot of unnecessary expenditures, human suffering, and loss of life for no apparent purpose. Even if they overestimate the amount of unnecessary surgery by 50 percent or even 75 percent, the toll in unnecessary suffering, death, and cost is still inexcusably high.

But as we shall see in the third chapter, the central question hinges on what is meant by unnecessary surgery and who will have the power to define it. And in many ways, defining what is unnecessary surgery is not as much a medical question as it first appears. True, there is nearly always a medical question at the base of it. Will surgery relieve someone of a life-threatening episode, or from death? Will it relieve him of pain or a non-life-threatening discomfort or disfigurement? Or may it do nothing for him or even harm him? Thus, the medical questions shade off into personal and social questions about what is important to people and how likely surgery is to enhance the chance of being helped in important ways.

The term reflecting this value orientation is "the quality of life." Before turning to look at the quality of life issue as regards surgery, we need to explore briefly the growing concern with attempts to control unnecessary surgery. Again the subcommittee seemed impressed with Dr. McCarthy's findings that elective surgery was deemed unnecessary in nearly one out of five cases where workers were told their surgery would not be paid for it they did not get a second opinion from an appropriate surgical specialist. And over 34 percent of the orthopedic consultants did not confirm the first doctor's opinions; neither did 29 percent of the urologists, 21 percent of the gynecologists or ophthalmologists, or 13 percent of the general surgeons. Other doctors recommended a second opinion program to the subcommittee also. One was Dr. Sidney Wolfe, who suggested that second consultations be handled by independent practitioners and be mandatory for both Medicaid (for the indigent) and Medicare (for the elderly) patients.

Second opinion programs are neither new nor unsuccessful in reducing health care costs and needless operations. In the words of Spencer Klaw, author of *The Great American Medicine Show:*

The likelihood that at least one out of every five or six operations in the United States is medically unjustified is also suggested by the results of a program put into operation in the 1950s by the United Mine Workers. Worried about the large sums it was spending for surgery for its members, the union stipulated that in the future all operations would have to be approved in advance by a qualified surgical specialist if the union was to pay for them. Appendectomies fell off by 60 percent, and hysterectomies by 75 percent; surgical procedures of all kinds declined by 17 percent.

On December 3, 1975, Blue Cross and Blue Shield of Greater New York announced a program of second professional opinions to confirm the necessity for elective procedures. While nearly all saw it as a possible way to cut costs, there was divided opinion as to whether it would hurt or improve the quality of medical care.

Many leaders of organized medicine, such as the AMA and local and state medical societies, have argued two things. For one, they have argued that reports of unnecessary surgery are greatly exaggerated; they have also argued that second opinions are not necessarily any more valid than first opinions.

For example, Dr. Ralph Emerson, president of the Medical Society of the state of New York, and Dr. John Creedon have said that standard or "present" criteria for determining the necessity of surgery are better than second opinions. They report that use of sound preestablished criteria shows there is less than 1 percent unnecessary surgery. Using "present criteria predictors," Dr. Emerson found that the incidence of unjustified surgery among 833 consecutive operations reviewed at twelve hospitals in Brooklyn and Long Island was less than 1 percent. He argued that McCarthy's study was "based on the false premise that a differing opinion justified the conclusion of 24 percent unnecessary surgery." He continued: "This is illogical and unscientific. The peer consultation concept has been discredited as an acceptable methodology of quality evaluation of medical and surgical care." Emerson and Creedon say their study provides "hard data to restore the public's confidence, as well as refute and defuse the unwarranted hysteria alleging a high degree of unjustified surgery."

In contrast, Dr. James H. Sammons, the AMA's executive vice president, has stated he rejects both established criteria and second opinions as a sound basis for determining the need for surgery. "It is not the disease which determines whether the procedure is an emergency but rather the condition of the patient and the time and circumstances under which the patient is seen by the physician," said Dr. Sammons. He argued for a "flexible approach" such as the guidelines used by Professional Standards Review Organizations rather than inflexible criteria.

Dr. Sammons also believes the medical profession is "virtually unanimous in the belief that an opinion of 'non-confirmed' by a consultant cannot be equated with 'unnecessary' surgery, 'deferred' surgery, 'surplus' surgery or any other such word one chooses to use at the moment." According to Sammons, "Such an equation is neither medically sound nor scientifically valid. . . ."

Sammons and other physicians do not necessarily question the use of second opinions. They had better not, since the eighth principle of the AMA's Principles of Medical Ethics states: "A physician should seek consultation upon request; in doubtful or difficult cases; or whenever it appears that the quality of medical services may be enhanced thereby."

But Sammons, like some other physicians, argues that a second judgment is "a professional but inescapably subjective judgment." In order for the subcommittee's findings to be valid, Sammons said "it must be assumed that in every instance of disagreement the opinion of the consultant must be the correct one." Dr. Sammons concludes with some other leaders of organized medicine that mandatory second opinions are "an arbitrary device to ration medical care."

Dr. Ralph Emerson sees a more insidious plot behind the government's use of such statistics. While researchers say their findings are preliminary and not generalizable to the whole United States population, "overzealous planners and politicians" use such "questionable statistics in their desire to influence social reform in medicine."

Proponents of the Kennedy version of National Health Insurance, especially the labor organizations, parrot the theme that the present system of fee-for-service is self-serving and is the cause of unnecessary or unjustified surgery in this country. ... Therefore, they say, we must restructure the entire health care delivery system in the image of the Kennedy legislation of a massive, federal, centralized system.

Second and contrary opinions, even when made by board-certified surgical consultants, do not necessarily mean that all surgery they advise against is unneeded; but it certainly raises questions about it. Since patients could get third, fourth, fifth opinions, etc., does this mean that the necessity or advisability of surgery is no more than some kind of professional, but nevertheless, subjective opinion?

New light was thrown on this question by the publication of a recent book, *Costs, Risks and Benefits of Surgery*. Instead of trying to answer the questions of when surgery is necessary or valuable by rhetoric, the authors call for a scientific study of surgery in which its risks and costs are compared to its benefits in a variety of areas. At the press conference announcing the publication of the book, the editors, John Bunker, Benjamin Barnes, and Frederick Mosteller, pointed out that the thirty-four contributors saw the need for better information on the costs and benefits of surgery if intelligent public policy is to guide its use. They wanted to find out in what ways and under what circumstances surgery contributed to an improved "quality of life."

"It is unfortunate that the debate on what is, and what is not, necessary surgery or necessary medical practice in general, has been joined as though the outcome will reflect on the competence of physicians," declared Dr. Howard Hiatt, at the news conference. Dr. Hiatt is from the Harvard public health school and wrote the foreword to the book. "Some procedures are, of course, 'necessary'—indeed, life saving. But most fall into the category where assessment of usefulness can be made only after very careful measurement of costs, risks and benefits," he said.

At the news conference Dr. Hiatt also pointed out that the decision making that goes on in surgery today is largely made "by the physician on the basis of his personal experience and his reading and interpretation of articles in the medical literature. What is needed," he argued, "is an aggregation of the broader experience of doctors throughout the country, an analysis of these data, and their translation into medical practice."

Dr. John Bunker, professor of anesthesia and of family, community, and preventive medicine at Stanford University, pointed out there was a "bias" on the part of both the medical profession and the public "to do more rather than less." But he said the cost squeeze has reached the point "where we can't just simply go with more is better any longer."

At the news conference Dr. Benjamin Barnes, associate professor of surgery at Harvard Medical School, said, "At the core of this issue of so-called unnecessary surgery is the need for more information as to the effectiveness of surgical therapies. The controversy persists," he commented, "in the absence of firm facts which are essential for the credible resolution of strong disagreements repeated in public and private testimony. In short, we must determine how 'unnecessary' some operations are."

Costs, Risks and Benefits of Surgery is a calm appraisal of when and under what conditions surgery is beneficial. Using cost-benefit analysis, the authors of this book look at the financial costs, and the risks and benefits, in terms of the *quantity* of life and the *quality* of life by comparing surgical and medical treatments to going without treatment. In a sense, they develop master equations for determining the relative worth of surgery for a given condition at a given time of life.

In this book, for example, Clark Abt takes a theoretical case, a forty-year-old female with a normal life expectancy of thirty-five more years.

Assuming that a year of life is worth $20,000 at this age (double the $10,000 a year we "pay to keep people alive in nursing homes"), should this woman have a simple mastectomy for breast cancer? To illustrate this case, Abt assumes a life expectancy of two years without surgery and five years with it. He then attaches a dollar figure to most of the "psychosocial" costs and benefits of either going with or without the surgery.

The psychosocial costs for going without surgery include grief at impending death, the pain and suffering of terminal cancer, family conflict over the choice of therapy, and the grief from the impending description of family life. But there will be some benefits to going without surgery—mainly avoiding those costs. The costs of surgery include the dollar cost of the mastectomy, the possibility of dying from surgery, the grief about the loss of a body part, the pain from surgery, the inconvenience of hospitalization, the possibility of not working for a month or two if employed, the possible limitation in active work, sports, and sex life, the worry over disfigurement and the recurrence of the disease, and the reduced aesthetic quality of life. On the other hand, there will be likely benefits from the surgery: reduced worry over impending death, the possibility of a longer, perhaps much longer, life to be used perhaps in the roles of wife, mother, and worker.

Abt finds that the simple mastectomy with five years life expectancy is preferable to two years life expectancy without mastectomy when all the risks and benefits are weighed, by a difference of $32,900. Thus, the probable extension of life by three years outweighs the psychosocial and financial costs associated with undergoing the surgery.

In evaluating any surgical technique, then, we need to compare outcomes to the risks inherent in that surgery and the costs of it. As indicated above, outcomes may be measured by how they change either the quantity of life or the quality of it. And changes in the quantity and quality of life do not necessarily go together. While mastectomies for breast cancer usually extend life, they often lower the quality of it. On the other hand, Dr. Bunker points out, an operation undertaken to correct an inguinal hernia on a sixty-five-year-old man, will, on the average, decrease his life expectancy by a few days but increase the quality of his life. But appendectomies done in the presence of minimal symptoms were found to be unnecessarily risky, costly, and damaging to the quality of life through hospitalization.

The relative payoff in the quality and quantity of life varies with both the procedure undertaken and the person undergoing it. Should a person with "minimally symptomatic gallstones" be treated medically (with drugs) or surgically (a cholecystectomy—gallbladder removal)? It depends on the patient, according to one study. On the average, a forty-four-year-old man in good preoperative condition would live sixteen days longer with the surgical treatment than with medical treatment. By age sixty the average advantage would be only seven days. However, a forty-nine-year-old man in poor preoperative condition would live thirty-three days longer on the average with the medical as opposed to surgical treatment. By age sixty the life expectancy would be lengthened by thirty-seven days if he chose the medical over the surgical treatment. On the other hand, the surgical treatment for such patients, while not extending their lives, may give them more relief from discomfort and disability.

Clearly then, "unnecessary surgery" is an ambiguous term. While there is much debate over its meaning and the extent to which it occurs, there is evidence that it does occur, as we shall see in succeeding chapters. But the critical question remains: when is surgery sufficiently beneficial in prolonging life and/or making it more satisfactory to justify the costs and risks of it?

Because patients have so little knowledge about the outcomes and risks of surgery, they usually defer to the advice of their doctor. Alex Gerber, M.D., writes: "The decision to operate is made solely by the surgeon. Overuse of surgical services in this country must therefore be attributed to poor surgeons rather than to informed or uninformed consumers...." He argues that we cannot wait for the public to become more informed to lower the prevalence of unnecessary operations. Rather, he says "a quicker and surer solution would be the stringent regulation of our hospitals so that only the qualified would be allowed to operate."

Surgery can and usually is beneficial in either extending the length or improving the quality of life. But sometimes it is not. We turn next to some case studies where it was neither.

2

CASE STUDIES IN UNNECESSARY SURGERY

The purest cases of unnecessary surgery are those undertaken solely for the financial gain of the physician. Nobody knows how often this happens. But it happens. Sometimes the cases are clear-cut. This occurs when the patient comes to or is referred to a surgeon because he is experiencing some pain or other difficulty. If there is absolutely no medical justification for the surgery because it will not cure the cause of the difficulty or alleviate the symptoms, then we have a clear case of unnecessary surgery. In such cases we have medical fraud. The operation is known to be unnecessary but is undertaken solely to benefit the physician.

One case was a woman who had had several miscarriages. She became pregnant again and became ill with stomach pains. Her physician diagnosed appendicitis. She refused to submit to surgery until the physician assured her that the surgery would not create any obstetrical problems. He did. Following surgery, she had a miscarriage and became mentally ill. At the trial the physician was accused of fraud. Several expert witnesses gave testimony that the pathology report had not confirmed appendicitis, and furthermore, that the risk of harm to the fetus was extremely high in contrast to what the operating surgeon had told her. Thus, the surgeon was found guilty of fraud because he had deliberately misstated the possibility of complications and did an operation that turned out to be unnecessary.

There are some cases of unnecessary surgery where the patient may be the cause more than the doctor. This occurs especially among what Dr.

William Nolen calls neurotics or "superneurotics"; many physicians call them "crocks." They are people in excellent physical health who refuse to be well because they enjoy their ailments so much. Doctors often refer them to other doctors to "get them off their backs." Often they send them to the "white-tower clinics," or university hospitals. According to Nolen:

When this happens the superneurotic often winds up undergoing an unnecessary operation. One patient with vague abdominal pains, who I and every other doctor in town knew was simply neurotic, underwent a complicated blood vessel operation to improve circulation in her intestine; another, whose current complaint was "tingling" in her hands, had her wrists operated on to relieve pressure on the nerves. Six months after their operations both patients were back in their family doctors' offices with new nebulous complaints. The operations hadn't helped them at all.

Such patients, according to Nolen, you can either brush off or overtreat.

Very little of what we are calling unnecessary surgery is probably ever detected by the patient. If it is detected and the patient wants to take legal action against the operating surgeon, quite often it will be done on the legal grounds of negligence or assault and battery. In negligence cases the patient must prove that the surgeon did not exercise due care in either the diagnosis or the treatment procedure. In assault and battery cases the patient must generally prove that the physician performed an operation on them to which they did not consent or performed a different kind of procedure from what they thought they had consented to.

The following story may not be untypical of the expense and pain incurred by a person subjected to a faulty diagnosis and treatment. It happened to Mrs. Dorothy O'Grady of Lauderhill, Florida, in 1963, who subsequently told the story to the House subcommittee investigating unnecessary surgery. This twenty-nine-year-old woman complained of back pains to her general practitioner. He admitted her to the hospital, where a series of tests were performed, and then called in a gynecologist as a consultant. But no x-rays were even taken of her back, the site of chronic pain. The gynecologist diagnosed her problem of back pain as due to a tumor of the right ovary. She underwent a hysterectomy in which her uterus and one ovary were removed.

But Mrs. O'Grady continued to suffer back pains as well as other problems. At a malpractice trial the court learned that the gynecologist had inadvertently injured her bladder during the operation. Thus, the first surgery led to the development of a vesicovaginal fistula (a fistula is an abnormal connection or passageway between two structures, in this case between the vagina and the bladder, that are normally separated). Mrs. O'Grady then had to undergo a second operation to repair her bladder and urinary tract obstruction. This led to financial problems. Her insurance carrier would not pay for the second surgery because it was due to a "pre-existing condition."

In spite of two operations, the second one an iatrogenic or doctor-induced problem, Mrs. O'Grady's backaches persisted. Her lawyer suggested she see an orthopedic specialist. She did. He diagnosed a structural back deformity which caused her left leg to be about one-quarter inch shorter than the right leg. When she started wearing a built-up shoe that he prescribed, the pain went away. She then brought suit against the gynecologist for negligent diagnosis that led to unnecessary surgery in the first place and for negligence in performing the surgery. And she had a clear legal basis for her suit—expert testimony that an incomplete examination led to the unnecessary surgery and that it was poorly performed.

Another case that the House subcommittee heard involved Mrs. Marie Valenzuela, her four children, and a niece. In 1969 she brought her youngest child, who had been running a high temperature, to her California physician who informed her that Linda would need a tonsillectomy. On a return visit and at the doctor's request, Mrs. Valenzuela brought along her other three children so he could examine their throats. In spite of their previously healthy throats, he determined that they needed tonsillectomies too. Accompanying Mrs. Valenzuela on this visit was a young niece who had occasionally been experiencing nosebleeds. After a brief examination the physician said this child also would need her tonsils removed.

In their conclusion on this case the House subcommittee reported:

The surgeries began, and one of Mrs. Valenzuela's children experienced brief respiratory difficulty but had no serious complications. Linda Valenzuela did not fare as well. Six days after being discharged from the hopsital, she began bleeding profusely from the neck and required three different surgical procedures. The operations left Linda with half the normal cerebral blood circulation. She was very near death from the bleeding, developed pneumonia, required a tracheotomy, and subsequently became anemic and contracted hepatitis. The loss of carotid circulation on one side increased the likelihood that sometime in the future Linda might experience brain damage. Laboratory tests determined that the operating physician had removed healthy tissue from each of the five children.

The Valenzuela children's experience in California is probably not unique. One physician reports some revealing differences about the rate at which tonsillectomies are performed in California. "Under the Medicaid program in California, tonsillectomies are performed on children below the age of sixteen almost twice as often as under some Blue Shield plans." But the difference is even much greater where physicians are salaried in group practice clinics. "The medically indigent children of California are having their tonsils removed at a *ten times higher* rate than are the patients at some group practice clinics which take care of non-indigent children." This physician concludes, "I am being conservative in suggesting, then, that we could greatly lower the incidence of tonsillectomy without damaging the health of American children."

In assault and battery cases expert physician testimony is often un-needed. In some cases a mistake is made in treating the wrong patient, or the physician does not secure the proper consent form. Then a patient or his lawyer can appeal to the *res ipsa loquitur* rule ("It speaks for itself"); this is invoked in those cases where expert physician testimony is not needed. Thus, if the wrong patient has a leg amputated, as actually occurred in one case, little if any expert testimony is needed with such self-evident material.

One woman sued a surgeon for fraudulent misrepresentation in the unnecessary removal of her spleen. She and her husband both testified that the surgeon had told them that her spleen was "hanging by a thread" and that it was "attached to her collar bone." She consented to surgery under the belief that the ligaments supporting the spleen would somehow be built up; instead the spleen was removed. The pathologist's report showed no abnormality in the organ itself. The court responded to the physician's plea that no expert testimony was given by saying none was needed. The quality of surgery was not under investigation; rather, the fact of surgical removal of the spleen when no consent was given for that procedure constituted assault and battery.

One man received a jury verdict of $56,000 because a surgeon had performed a cervical sympathectomy (a cutting of sympathetic nerves to reduce constriction in the blood vessels) without consent. The patient had entered the hospital with an injured right ankle but with none of the complaints (such as cold feet due to poor circulation) usually considered as prerequisite symptoms for justifying the surgery. A lay jury decided in favor of the man because the surgery was unjustified and unnecessary. And without the proper consent form being completed by the patient, the surgeon was found guilty of assault and battery.

Carelessness is sometimes the cause of needless surgery. This sad case is about a Florida woman who was admitted to a hospital for surgical biopsies of cysts in both breasts. The cysts were removed by a surgeon who told the nurse it was proper to put both specimens in the same jar because he was *sure* neither was malignant. The pathologist, a resident, found that one of the cysts was malignant. He then destroyed the biopsy specimens to the extent that he couldn't tell which specimen came from which breast. The surgeon removed both breasts and in turn was sued by the woman, who justifiably argued that one breast had been removed unnecessarily. The jury returned a $100,000 verdict, which was supported on appeal, against the careless doctor and the hospital (who employed the resident).

While some unnecessary operations are detected by patients, it is probably safe to say most are not. Dr. Alex Gerber, a California surgeon, reports that one day in the course of examining a young woman he questioned her about a scar on her stomach. "Oh," she said, "I had my uterus suspended when I was 18." Gerber said, "My ears pricked up; that is a most extraordinary operation for an 18 year old." The girl continued, "I was about to be married and my mother sent me to our family doctor for some premarital advice. . . . He checked me over and found that my uterus was tipped backward. He said I wouldn't be able to get pregnant unless it was fixed, so I had the operation two months before my wedding."

Dr. Gerber says the story had a happy ending because the woman later gave birth to a healthy baby girl. The doctor was pleased with his surgery, and his chart work was neat and satisfied the peer review committee at the hospital and thereby the Joint Commission on Accreditation of Hospitals, and since the doctor's fee was within the "usual and customary" fee bounds, the insurance carrier was happy to pay it. But what a waste—a needless operation, unnecessary suffering and risk, an undeserved fee. Dr. Gerber concludes:

But the fact is that the patient had been victimized by a physician who was flagrantly incompetent or dishonest, or both. The operation that had endangered her life was totally unnecessary. She would have gotten pregnant just as readily without it, and the outcome is not always so benign in such cases of "absurd surgery," as Dr. Elmer Hess, a onetime AMA president, called the performance of unnecessary uterine suspensions.

While some unnecessary surgery may be attributed to economic motives, some may be due to the poor or careless diagnostic habits of doctors. And a few cases may be attributed to the difficulty of making accurate diagnosis—particularly if the diagnosis takes time but to delay surgery might be critical. An example of the latter occurred in Oneida County, New York, in 1976, when at least twelve children had normal appendices removed at two hospitals over a period of three weeks. It turned out that they had yersiniosis, an intestinal disorder from a highly contagious bacterium, whose symptoms are nearly identical to those of appendicitis. While this relatively rare disease can be treated by antibiotics, two to four days are needed to diagnose the disease by laboratory methods, according to Dr. Daniel Stowens, director of St. Luke's Hospital in Utica, New York. The diagnoses in these cases were made by qualified surgeons who believed it would have been dangerous to ignore the symptoms. According to Dr. Stowens, the suspicion of yersiniosis dawned only after two or three of the children were found to have normal appendices.

Howard and Martha Lewis tell of an interesting episode in a Passaic, New Jersey, hospital a number of years ago. This hospital had a particularly high rate of emergency surgery. Some doctors at the hospital wondered how much of it was unnecessary—prompted either by the desire for money or by poor diagnosis rather than by medical necessity. To find out, they formed a committee to inspect tissue removed during surgery. And what they found was startling: "Fully one out of every three operations performed at the hospital was unnecessary—the organs taken out were normal." Because of the limitations of diagnostic accuracy, perhaps no more than 10 percent of the operations in which tissue is removed for signs of pathology should be normal. According to the Lewises, "Many surgeons have an erroneous diagnostic rate of not more than 6 percent. The American College of Surgeons allows a margin of error of 12 percent before it levels a charge of unnecessary surgery." The tissue committee warned the worst offenders. Before long questionable operations dropped to an acceptable rate.

Unjustified surgery allegations are probably leveled most frequently at appendectomies, hysterectomies, and tonsillectomies. Doctors and others have come up with clever terms to describe these: "chronic remunerative appendicitis," "the rape of the pelvis," "hip-pocket hysterectomies," and "dollarectomies."

Howard and Martha Lewis tell of two surgeons at one small hospital pitted against the other physicians, who were concerned that they were too quick with the knife. The medical staff set up a tissue committee to inspect removed tissue for signs of pathology. But the two errant surgeons would not recognize its decisions. The trustees of the hospital then asked the American College of Surgeons to audit the hospital's surgical track record.

For five days the College investigators did an on-the-spot study of the 879 surgical operations performed during the preceding 14 months. The investigators found that the two surgeons in question churned out more than half the surgery done at the hospital. No less than 24 percent of their surgery was unnecessary, constituting about one operation of every eight performed at the hospital.

Currently an efficacy study is being carried out at two Pittsburgh hospitals to determine how helpful a tonsillectomy and adenoidectomy done separately or in combination are in relieving children of throat-related illnesses. The directors of this study, Drs. Charles Bluestone and Jack Paradise, point out that such operations account for about 50 percent of all major surgical operations on children and 10 percent of the hospital bed days utilized by children. They found puzzling wide variations in the frequency of the operations in different sections of the county, suggesting the criteria for doing this operation were not at all uniform. To date they have found that about 60 percent of the children being sent to them for this operation do not qualify for it at all. Of the remaining 40 percent of the cases, only about one fourth of the referred children needed the operation in the next two years. In his testimony before a government subcommittee, Dr. Bluestone pointed out that many of these operations were being performed by non-board-certified surgeons who, in his opinion, used less critical indications for the surgery than board-certified surgeons.

Small hospitals or privately owned hospitals may be the location where a lot of unnecessary surgery occurs in America. This is because in many small hospitals the surgeon or two working there do not have their surgery as closely monitored as do surgeons operating in large hospitals. In fact, the physician monitoring a case may be the same as the one treating it. And private unaccredited hospitals that do not have to meet the standards of the Joint Commission on Hospital Accreditation are also more likely to have surgical practices that are not audited by tissue committees, and they are less likely to have utilization review committees to review the necessity for admitting a patient, treating him, or keeping him beyond a time typical for his condition.

A frightening example of what can happen in small run-for-profit hospitals was turned up by William Haines, an investigative reporter for the *Chicago Tribune.* As part of a team investigating the practices of hospitals and doctors in Chicago, he took a job as a janitor in the private, for-profit, 100-bed Von Solbrig Hospital on the southwest side of Chicago. This route was taken, he says, because "doctors, we found, were unwilling to speak critically of other doctors' practices. Medical records were confidential." As a janitor he was sometimes abruptly called into the operating room to help move a patient from a surgery table to a cart to be wheeled out. He reported there was "no registered nurse regularly assigned to the surgery room." His testimony before a house subcommittee inspecting the evidence of unnecessary surgery and the quality of surgery is revealing. Haines told the subcommittee:

Many of the surgery patients were public aid recipients on Medicaid. They were brought to the hospital by Dr. E. J. Mirmelli, who ran a clinic in a low-income black neighborhood on Chicago's west side.

What was the most surprising about the surgery on these patients was the large number of tonsillectomies performed. I had been warned about it the first day I went to work at the hospital. . . . I soon found that it was quite common for entire families to be scheduled for tonsillectomies the same morning.

Two families of five children had their tonsils taken out on different mornings within two weeks.

On May 15, 1975, five brothers had their tonsils and adenoids removed and among them were three circumcisions, an umbilical hernia, and the removal of a cyst.

The work was done by one doctor within six hours and Medicaid was billed $2,647.32. Dr. Mirmelli was shown to have collected $124,000 from Medicaid in one year.

The mother of the five boys who had their tonsils out that morning told us that her children never got high fevers, loss of hearing or ear drainage, the symptoms we were told to look for. She said that they did all get colds and sore throats in the winter.
. . . .

We found such an occurrence was frequent. In 2 weeks Mirmelli performed 14 tonsillectomies.

One mother told us that she took her three sons to Dr. Mirmelli for circumcisions when he abruptly told her they would also all need their tonsils out. He scheduled them for surgery but she made him cancel the tonsillectomies.

Another woman said Mirmelli had scheduled all six of her children for tonsillectomies but she refused to let him perform them.

Curious about the likelihood of five members of the same family needing tonsillectomies at the same time, Haines asked a number of throat specialists and surgeons about the probability of such an event. Their responses were, "It's ridiculous. The odds are astronomical"; "That would be very incredible"; "One in a million"; "One in a hundred million"; and, "Oh, good grief." Later on in his testimony reporter Haines said:

It was interesting to us that costs of the hospital stay were increased by many tests. I think anyone who has seen a hospital bill expects that; but what was not expected was that children were always given EKG's when they came in for tonsil surgery. Our experts laughed at the idea of giving 6-year-olds EKG's.

There were X-rays and laboratory costs. There were separate charges for operating room, delivery room and recovery room, although surgery there was often one sweeping operation from the patient's bed to surgery and back to his bed.

The Chicago Board of Health ordered Von Solbrig Hospital closed pending hearings. Meanwhile the State sued Dr. Charles Von Solbrig to remove his medical license on the grounds that he ran an unsafe hospital. He voluntarily turned in his license, closed down the hospital, and retired.

As we shall note in later chapters, surgeons vary in their treatment philosophy. Some are aggressive, or liberally inclined toward surgery; others see it more as a last resort when a more conservative "medical" approach does not appear to be working. For example, Marcia Millman in *The Unkindest Cut* says that the chief of surgery felt residents at one teaching hospital were considered too "daring" because they wanted to gain experience. "In order to demonstrate their masculinity they were always daring one another into doing the most drastic procedure available in any situation." From his viewpoint, he also felt many private doctors "were just as stupidly aggressive as the residents." On the other hand, many of the residents felt he was an "anti-surgery surgeon" because he didn't take action fast enough. But it may be that some surgeons are too knife-happy, too quick for the good of their patients, and tell them too little about what is going on.

"One surgeon, for example, suspected that an elderly patient had pancreatic cancer, and he told her that an exploratory operation should be performed immediately, the next day if possible," Marcia Millman reports. But when told of this, the patient became extremely upset. The surgeon then arranged for the woman to have a psychiatric consultation. After talking to the woman the psychiatrist urged the surgeon to postpone the exploratory operation for a week, believing the patient's symptoms might either go away or be explained in some other way. He told the surgeon this would not change her prognosis. Furthermore, by waiting they might avoid subjecting the woman to this experience she dreaded. Millman continues: "The surgeon agreed with the psychiatrist's reasoning, but refused to delay the surgery. He maintained that the patient needed to have complete confidence in him, and that if he were to change the plan, it might jeopardize her faith in him." What happened? According to Millman, "The surgical exploration turned out to reveal nothing but a benign mass that would have disappeared by itself."

In the spring of 1976 Dr. R. B., a Massachusetts physician, was notified that he would be suspended from the Medicaid program for three years because of alleged procedural violations uncovered by the Massachusetts Welfare Department. At the same time a panel of physicians formally charged him with many instances of "unjustified surgery and poor medical care." He practiced surgery at the eighty-four-bed Revere hospital even though the hospital had not met state licensure requirements for at least five years.

In the same year the State Welfare Department released a report enumerating actual case histories under Dr. R. B.'s supervision which showed, according to the panel of doctors, very questionable judgment. One fifty-three-year-old man was admitted with a severely inflamed stomach and a suspected heart attack. The initial blood pressure reading of 214 over 140 was in the range most physicians would consider life-threatening. Yet Dr. R. B. did not record later blood pressure readings and gave no treatment for the man's extremely high blood pressure. In another case, a forty-eight-year-old man was admitted for thirteen days with a suspected heart attack and concussion. The hospital records on the man showed that no admission orders were written until the fifth day and no evidence was available that Dr. R. B., the admitting physician, ever saw the man.

The panel of six doctors and four laymen who reviewed a random sample of Dr. R. B.'s cases was under the auspices of the state-funded policing mechanism called CHAMP (Ceritified Hospital Admissions Monitoring Program). In their report they enumerated other cases of poor and questionably necessary care. One was that of an eighteen-year-old girl who was admitted with a diagnosis of frequent and heavy menstrual bleeding. The diagnosis raised a question about the presence of a pelvic inflammatory disease indicating widespread infection of the female organs. The panel found no justification for the diagnosis inasmuch as her blood count was normal and she had never been subjected to a pelvic examination. She underwent tubal irrigation, a procedure which can spread pelvic inflammatory disease through the abdominal cavity. The panel found the medical history, physical exam record, and progress notes "untimely and inadequate."

Another case involved a twenty-four-year-old woman who was admitted twice. The first diagnosis was for a bladder infection that was never substantiated by laboratory data. Nevertheless, Dr. R. B. performed a tonsillectomy on her in the presence of tonsillitis, a practice condemned as hazardous by most doctors. On her second visit she was diagnosed as having heavy menstrual bleeding. Dr. R. B. performed a total hysterectomy on her (removal of the uterus), as well as removing both ovaries and her appendix. The reviewing panel concluded, "The reason for the hysterectomy was unsupported by the record and the pathology report contained a gross description of a normal uterus, tube and ovaries." The panel also declared that the removal of this young woman's reproductive organs "did not appear necessary."

Still another case reported on by the panel questioned the necessity of Dr. R. B.'s surgery in her situation. This twenty-year-old woman was admitted with a suspicion of pelvic inflammatory disease which was subsequently confirmed by laboratory findings. But when she underwent a dilation and currettage, a scraping of the uterine lining, Dr. R. B. also inserted an intrauterine device. The panel found this practice questionable because the insertion of a foreign body into an infected area can break down the body's defenses against infection. Moreover, she underwent an operation that might seriously affect her ability to have children, called conization of the cervix, a removal of tissue from the mouth of the uterus. "This procedure," reported the panel, "is usually indicated only where cancer has been diagnosed."

When Richard J. Feeley, assistant commissioner of public health in Massachusetts, saw the report, he said he was upset by the finding that R. B. exhibited a tendency to remove the reproductive organs of young women who complained of menstrual problems. "I was grossed out," he said, in finding that Dr. R. B. was "doing hysterectomies on 22 and 24 year old women who showed no signs of cancer."

Dr. R. B. reportedly was doing about half the surgery at the Revere hospital and was responsible for many of the Medicaid admissions to it. Since he was put on probation for Medicaid billing abuses in the prior year, some of his surgical load has been reduced, according to reporter Richard Knox. The CHAMP investigating committee found other things wrong at the hospital—excessive laboratory testing when none was indicated, such as two electrocardiograms on a twenty-year-old woman with nonsuspected heart disease, excessive prescription of sedative and narcotic drugs, and inadequate laboratory testing to verify tentative diagnosis. The CHAMP investigation was launched after the State Welfare Department's continuing review of Medicaid admissions turned up excessive lengths of stay as well as "gross abuse of patient care." Incidentally, the Welfare Department reported that Dr. R. B. had engaged in some deceptive and fraudulent practices. For instance, he billed for hospital visits before the patients got there and after they were discharged.

As we shall see in chapters 4, 5, and 6, one of the critical factors in how much surgery is undertaken originates in what Doctors Alan Gittelsohn and John Wennberg call the "physician factor." They do not define this very well except to say it has to do with the "characteristics of the providers," such as a proclivity to find surgery indicated even when others would disagree with their judgment. But their findings are nearly self-explanatory. They studied 6,356 tonsillectomy and adenoidectomy procedures performed in Vermont by ninety-two physicians over a three-year period, 1969–71. At one end of the scale were thirty-six doctors who together did only ninety tonsillectomies and adenoidectomies over the three-year period. At the other end were two doctors who respectively did 429 and 462 tonsillectomies and adenoidectomies in the same period. Three other busy doctors did 373, 389, and 395 such operations. Together these five doctors removed 32 percent of the tonsils and adenoids excised in the state in a three-year period! There was no evidence that the children who came to these five doctors had more tonsil and adenoid problems than children visiting other doctors in the state. Could it be that such wide differences in diagnostic appraisal were due to some factor other than medical need?

As I was writing this book, people would ask me what I was working on. When I told them I was writing a book on "unnecessary surgery," almost invariably they would tell me of a personal incident involving themselves or a friend. One man I talked to was an insurance salesman. A number of years ago, he said, he suffered from low back pain after an accident. He went to an orthopedist. "He told me I had a slipped disc and that I'd have back pain until I had it operated on," he said. "But I'm afraid of surgery. I went to another orthopedist. He told me I was lucky. He said I didn't need surgery but simply had a pulled muscle." I asked him what happened with his back. He said the back pain went away slowly, and he does not have any problem now.

When I told the librarian at one hospital about the nature of my research, she pointed out that sometimes unnecessary surgery is wanted by a person who is not medically informed. She told me of a friend of hers who was experiencing some menstrual bleeding. "She decided she wanted a hysterectomy. She visited several doctors but they told her she didn't need one," she reported. "But she finally found a doctor who would give her one. And she almost died from the operation."

Anecdotes abound, and of course may not be entirely trustworthy. But the story of Dr. John G. Nork, whose California butcheries recently came to light, shocked the world. The case that brought Dr. Nork to court and eventually to being thrown out of medical practice was brought by Albert Gonzales against both Dr. Nork and Mercy General Hospital of Sacramento, California. The trial involved a cast of eighty-four characters and lasted twenty-two weeks. It resulted in a $3.7 million judgment against Mercy Hospital and Dr. Nork. The court ordered the negligent physician and the hospital where he had staff privileges to pay $1.7 million in compensatory damages. The physician was ordered to pay $2 million in punitive damages.

It all started in October, 1967, when Albert Gonzales's car was "rear-ended." The plaintiff was described as a sober, industrious, athletic, family man. He moonlighted, at age 25, to help support his family. After the accident he experienced some pain in his back and neck but continued light work for several day. On November 1, 1967, he consulted Dr. Nork, a non-board-certified orthopedist.

Dr. Nork said he needed a laminectomy, an operation involving the removal of a small portion of bone of the spine, usually done in order to reach and remove a spinal disk or tumor. The findings, in the words of the superior court judge who wrote a 196-page memorandum on the case, follow:

Dr. Nork's treatment of the plaintiff was in accordance with the pattern of professional misconduct. . . . He performed a perfunctory examination of Gonzales, made no substantial effort to treat the patient conservatively, discouraged consultation, hurried him into unnecessary surgery, which he bungled, and achieved a bad result, which he concealed. . . . In a nutshell: Dr. Nork not only harmed Gonzales' back, but he also ruined his personality. And he is liable for the bodily harm resulting from the emotional disturbance caused by his misconduct.

In the course of this five-month trial it was pointed out that Gonzales was paralyzed from the waist down as a result of the operation. Being an invalid destroyed him physically and emotionally. As a result of his being unable to adjust to his invalidism, he became deeply depressed; his depression resulted in several attempts at suicide and in episodes of severe alcohol abuse. He was in continual and intense pain and subject to emotional disturbances. Being unable to work, or to play with his children, and suffering impotency, he became separated from his wife. Understandably, he had become distrustful of physicians. He also subsequently suffered cancer of the testicles. But after an orchiectomy (removal of the testicles), the cancer was found to have metastasized and to be inoperable. While the judge did not explicitly rule on the cause of cancer, it was estimated there was only a 20 percent probability of his surviving for as long as three years.

Dr. Nork gave the appearance of a successful doctor. Fellow doctors and nurses thought he was successful because he was so busy. But at the trial he admitted that, in the words of the court, "he treated other patients improperly [as substantiated] by the appalling list of patients on whom he performed surgery that was either unnecessary or bungled, or both." According to the court, "Evidence was adduced as to 38 patients and, since several underwent multiple surgeries, something in excess of 50 operations that were unneeded or botched."

Delving into his background, the court found that he was a respected member of the hospital staff before his fraud was detected in 1970. Some of his patients included hospital employees and medical staff. He had completed a three-year residency in orthopedic surgery, followed by four years in the Air Force, where he practiced his specialty. He migrated to California after his military service. But in 1965, 1966, and 1967 he failed to pass his examinations for board certification as an orthopedic surgeon.

Although he appeared to have a successful practice, at the trial a public accountant testified that during 1967 and 1968 creditors were after him and that Nork undertook unnecessary surgery to avoid action by them. In addition to finding that he used "upper" and "downer" drugs, the court also found that he overcharged and that he was professionally motivated for financial gain "with evil purpose . . . [he] for nine years made a practice of performing unnecessary surgery, and performing it badly, simply to line his pockets."

Another important aspect of this case was that the hospital was judged liable for part of the damages because it had not sufficiently monitored the doctor's behavior. In 1962 Dr. Nork reported "complications" in a case whose adequate review would have shown that the quality of care he gave to patients was patently below an acceptable standard. In 1963 a patient undertook a joint malpractice case against Dr. Nork and the hospital (subsequently dismissed) that normally would have been investigated by the hospital staff. At the trial Reed J. Nesbitt, an M.D. and an assistant director of the Joint Commission on Accreditation of Hospitals, testified that a "prudent hospital" would investigate any physician who is the basis of a malpractice suit.

In 1966 Dr. Nork unwittingly excised nerve fibers in another laminectomy case. While this was routinely referred to the hospital pathologist, he in turn did not report it to the medical audit and tissue committee. But it should have been done, because, according to one witness at the trial, the removal of such fibers constitutes a "discrepancy" that under medical staff bylaws in accredited hospitals is to be reviewed by the committee.

At the trial, and after Dr. Nork was dismissed from the staff of Mercy Hospital in 1970 (at about the same time he lost his malpractice insurance), the hospital was found to be operating an inadequate peer review system to detect fraud and incompetence. The court criticized the hospital for assuming that Dr. Nork was telling the truth when in fact he was distorting medical records and avoiding consultations. The court found that case reviews were infrequent, casual, uncritical, and sandwiched in between other activities that were seen to be more pressing. No profile was kept on the doctor's record or on discrepancies noted in the records or nurses' notes. Dr. Nesbitt also pointed out that peer review audits are usually carried out in a clubroom atmosphere where economic pressures and a fear of reprisals keep doctors from being critical of one another.

I have read a lot of malpractice cases. Dr. John Nork's is probably the worst one, because it is not simply a case of poor medical judgment or oversight. Some errors are bound to happen in the practice of every physician, most of whom see about five thousand patients a year. But the case of Albert Gonzales is terrifying because, in the words of the presiding judge, it "was simply an incident in the execution of a systematic scheme of fraud." Other patients were terrified by Nork, and some of them ended up maimed. How many cases there were besides the thirty-eight cases of unnecessary or bungled surgery that came to light will never be known.

Most doctors are not only highly trained for the procedures they undertake but are conscientious about the welfare of their patients. They want to help people while earning a good living. But a few, maybe 1 percent or maybe 5 percent—the estimates vary considerably—are not competent to the tasks they undertake, or may be motivated by the wrong reasons. Their performance in many cases may not only not help the patient, they may gravely injure him. As we shall see in succeeding chapters, defining unnecessary surgery is a very difficult task. Despite that, it does occur, as our case studies have shown. And it takes a toll. It takes a toll on patients who are unwittingly, and sometimes wittingly, exploited, and it takes a toll on all of us, doctors and patients alike, who indirectly pay for unnecessary care and higher malpractice insurance. And it takes a toll on the medical profession, for the questionable practices of a few harm the prestige of all.

3

UNNECESSARY SURGERY—WHAT
DO YOU MEAN?

Taken at face value, the term "unnecessary surgery" seems clear. It is surgery that is unneeded. But then, when is something needed? And needed for what? Perhaps the distinction between emergency and elective surgery will be somewhat helpful here. Emergency surgery is that which is undertaken in life-threatening or life-damaging circumstances. While it is often undertaken to save a life, it may, on occasion, be performed to save a limb or an eye. As the term suggests, it must be undertaken immediately if a person's life or overall health is to be saved. Rarely is emergency surgery unnecessary. But it can be if a faulty diagnosis is made.

Elective surgery, on the other hand, is that which is undertaken at a time convenient or suitable to the patient and the doctor for a condition that may be improved by surgery. However, if the patient does not get the surgery, his life may not be in much danger. Allegations made about unnecessary surgery usually refer to elective surgery.

While these two terms are commonly used and make helpful distinctions, they remain rather crude categories. A surgeon, Robert E. Rothenberg, points out that most conscious patients first inquire of their surgeons, "Is this operation necessary?" They usually follow this question with a second, "And what will happen if I'm not operated on?" In answering, according to Rothenberg, a surgeon will usually tell his patient that his condition falls into one of the following five categories.

1. *"Emergency Surgery:* Conditions demanding immediate attention."

Some examples of conditions demanding immediate attention are fractured skulls, stabbings or gunshot wounds, extensive burns, severe lacerations, an obstruction of the urinary bladder, an acute intestinal obstruction, a ruptured ulcer, a clot in a major blood vessel, a major bone fracture, acute glaucoma, acute appendicitis, a strangulated hernia, a ruptured pregnancy, and gangrene. There are degrees to most of these conditions. Without immediate attention, the patient is under a life-threatening episode that could result in death or severe impairment, to say nothing of the pain he might be experiencing.

2. *"Urgent surgery:* Conditions requiring prompt attention. The patient should arrange for hospital admission within 24 to 48 hours." Examples of conditions requiring prompt attention are organ cancers, kidney or ureteral stones, mastoid infections, obstructing ulcers of the stomach or duodenum, bleeding hemorrhoids, twisted ovarian cysts, and acute gallbladder infections.

3. *"Required Surgery:* Conditions that must be operated upon but do not demand immediate attention or prompt action. The patient should arrange for hospital admission at some time within a period of a few weeks or months." Some examples of what Rothenberg calls "required surgery" conditions are eye cataracts, spinal fusions, sinus operations, corrections of bone deformities, simple ovarian cysts, prostate conditions without obstruction, artery replacement, repair of heart and blood vessel defects, and inflammation of the gallbladder without acute infection. The time requirement is more open for treating these conditions. However, I would disagree that all these conditions "require surgery." Require by whose standards? And by what standards? Undoubtedly, people could live with some of these conditions if they were willing to accept discomfort and other limitations such as blindness. On the other hand, these conditions should be operated upon if the individual wants to maintain or achieve optimal health or if he wants to improve the quality of his life or perhaps extend it.

4. *"Elective Surgery:* Conditions that should be operated upon, but in all probability, failure to have the surgery performed will not result in catastrophe." Such conditions include cleft palate and harelip operations, simple hemorrhoids, superficial cysts, simple hernias without danger of strangulation, nongrowing fatty or fibrous tumors, and the repair of burn scars.

5. *"Optional Surgery:* Conditions for which surgery is advisable but not essential." Illustrative conditions here are strabismus (crossed eyes),

cosmetic surgery, breast reconstruction after a mastectomy (breast removal), varicose vein operations, and the removal of warts.

This fivefold ranking of the seriousness of conditions that warrant surgery is helpful in pointing out that both health and illness range along a lengthy continuum. At one end of the continuum is a comatose condition where the bedridden patient does not consciously carry out meaningful activities. Except for certain body processes taking place which maintain life, like a heart beating and lungs breathing, the person is dead. At the other end of the continuum is "health." As defined by the World Health Organization, "Health is a state of complete physical, mental and social well being and not merely the absence of disease or infirmity." Thus, in a variety of ways, according to Walter Greene, health is a relative concept. It is relative to one's time in history, to one's age, to self-expectations and the expectations of others, to emotional satisfaction, and to a sense of physical well being. Rather than being a static quality, it is a dynamic process undergoing constant change.

The relativity of health and illness makes it difficult then to define what is unnecessary surgery. Surgeons have wrestled with this problem too. In their summary report, *Surgery in the United States,* the American College of Surgeons and the American Surgical Association agreed there was a need for a precise definition of unnecessary operations. Their report (SOSSUS) states:

It is commonly alleged that large numbers of operations carried out in the United States are unnecessary. Several categories of operations might be termed "unnecessary," depending upon their individual clinical frame of reference and, in many cases, on individual evaluation of the patient or the patient's record. There are variations in degree of necessity, whether medical, personal, or social.

We shall return to this statement after we look at the six categories of unnecessary operations the American College of Surgeons and the American Surgical Association developed. These six categories are similar to the ones that Dr. George Zuidema presented in testimony to the Subcommittee on Oversight and Investigations of the Committee on Interstate and Foreign Commerce which investigated unnecessary surgery.

"Category 1. *Completely discretionary operations for asymptomatic non-pathologic, non-threatening disorders.*" This is a complicated description for cosmetic and reconstructive surgery on the nose, eye, lips, ears, face, breast, buttocks, and other parts of the body. As we shall see in a later chapter, rarely is such surgery directly necessary for the physical health of a person. But there will be widely varying degrees to which it may affect the psychological health of a person and indirectly thereby his physical well being and his social well being. Nonetheless, as the SOSSUS report states it, "When only vanity is served, however, necessity must be placed at a far lower level."

"Category 2. *Operations where no pathologic tissue is removed.*" For many types of surgery where tissue is removed, the justification is that the tissue was pathological. To determine its nature a hospital pathologist often examines it. If the tissue was nonpathological, then the surgery was unnecessary. But several limitations need to be set to this definition. One is that some operations do not involve the removal of tissue and therefore this category is inappropriate. Some examples of this type of operation are normal obstetrical delivery, a hysterectomy for profuse and continuous bleeding, the reduction of fractures, elimination of intestinal fistulae (abnormal passageways), arterial reconstruction, and a vagotomy (severing the vagus nerve to the stomach) for an ulcer. A second limitation or complication for this category is that sometimes the preoperative diagnosis would suggest the presence of pathological tissue. Take appendicitis as an example. Most patients with appendicitis experience generalized cramps in the abdomen, nausea, vomiting, a rise in body temperature and then, about a day later, the localization and tenderness in the lower right abdomen and usually an increase in the white blood cell count. But about 15 percent of all cases of appendicitis do now show all these symptoms or exhibit the typical progression of events. In such nontypical cases it may be better to risk an exploratory operation and take out the appendix even if it is not inflamed than to expose the patient to the higher risk of an untreated inflamed or ruptured appendix.

But should such an operation then be termed unnecessary? The American College of Surgeons generally accepts a 12 percent error rate in diagnosis in such cases because of some individual variation in pain thresholds, tolerance, and symptoms. Thus, if some tissue that is removed is nonpathological, it is not always an indication of unnecessary surgery. But if a surgeon's accuracy in diagnosis is only 60 percent in such cases, we have some evidence that either his diagnostic skills are poor and below acceptable standards or that he is operating for profit (category 6 below).

"Category 3. *Operations where indications are a matter of difference in judgment and opinion among experts.*" Since the practice of medicine is both an art and a science, differing judgments in many areas suggest that it is sometimes more of an art. In this vein, the surgeon may or may not suggest or undertake a particular surgical procedure in light of his clinical experience and information. Thus, some surgeons are more "conservative" in their readiness to undertake surgery. They may prescribe a medical treatment for duodenal ulcers instead of or before the surgical option. Some otolaryngologists argue that no more than about 2 to 3 percent of all children need tonsillectomies, whereas the national rate appears to be around 20 to 30 percent, with wide local variations. The problem this presents in determining the amount of unnecessary surgery is, whose standards shall be accepted. If the conservative surgeons set the standards, then the rate and amount of unnecessary surgery will be higher, especially if they are judging those who are quick with the knife. On the other hand, if those who judge when surgery is necessary are those liberally inclined to surgery, then we might have low reports of unnecessary surgery or even "underutilization." While some surgeons hold, for example, that mastectomies are unnecessary because biopsies and perhaps radiotherapy and chemotherapy are the most appropriate treatment for breast cancer, others believe that mastectomies, sometimes radical in nature, are best. While there may be scientific answers in terms of survival rates with alternative procedures, clinical judgment and opinion still holds sway in many areas of surgery.

"Category 4. *Operations to alleviate endurable or tolerable differences.*" This category includes operations to relieve the early symptoms of prostatism in older men, minor varicose veins, mildly symptomatic gallstones, minor uterine bleeding, and perhaps some coronary artery bypass surgery. It resembles Rothenberg's "elective surgery" but may contain some of the kinds of operations he would include under "required surgery." But as with reconstructive and cosmetic surgery, the necessity of it depends not on physical survival value, but on what is important to the patient, as well as on his ability to pay for it. For example, take a person with mild claudication, an ailment characterized by pain and tenderness of the leg muscles when walking or exercising. The pain usually goes away upon resting a minute or two. It is thought to be due to a spasm, along with arteriosclerosis, of the arteries supplying the muscles of the legs. It can become severe and quite painful. While weight reduction, giving up smoking, and avoiding a high-cholesterol diet may help prevent it or reduce its severity, it can be treated in other ways. Some of the mild cases can be treated with a drug to relax arterial spasms. But if all else fails the person with mild or more severe claudication may want to get an artery bypass operation in his thighs or around the knee joints to overcome the circulation deficiency due to arteriosclerosis. Or, possibly, he could get a lumbar sympathectomy. This operation *sometimes* causes the blood vessels in the legs to dilate and carry more blood. Now, the question is, should such an operation be called unnecessary surgery for a person who has his lifestyle limited by claudication? What if he needs to do considerable walking in his job or he enjoys hiking or golfing? How one defines what is necessary, or conversely an "unnecessary" luxury, will reflect his education, his social setting, and his life goals.

"Category 5. *Operations formerly performed [but] . . . now considered outdated, obsolete or discredited.*" Some surgical procedures have been or should be abandoned because they have been found to be ineffective or have become obsolete with advances in information. Insofar as such operations are still performed, they are unnecessary. Examples of such operations are lumbodorsal sympathectomies for hypertension, certain back operations for the relief of low back pain, neurological neck operations for the treatment of asthma and emphysema, and uterine suspensions. 2060138

In May of 1977 Blue Shield announced that it would curb payment for twenty-eight surgical and diagnostic procedures now considered outmoded or useless. Eight different medical organizations, including the American College of Surgeons, had developed the initial list of eighteen surgical and ten diagnostic tests that doctors would no longer be reimbursed for unless they defended their claim in writing. This claim would then be examined by local physician review panels.

In developing an initial, not complete, list of technologies that they wanted to retire, Dr. Rollins Hanlon, director of the American College of Surgeons, said, "Our aim is quality, and if quality can be combined, as we think it can, with containment of costs, then it would be a good thing."

The extent to which individuals are subjected to dated surgical procedures bypassed by new surgical developments or none at all is unknown; but the very fact that Blue Shield initiated a national plan to curb such surgery suggests it is not limited to a few doctors. In any case, the fifth category is also clearly a case of unnecessary surgery.

"Category 6. *Operations done primarily for the personal gain of the surgeon, wherein the weight of informed opinion would deny any indication [for surgery] to be present.*" The SOSSUS report defines this money-motivated surgery in a more cryptic fashion: "If a surgeon carries out *operations for which there is little justification by clinical, x-ray or laboratory study,* the hospital staff committee should establish the requirement of preoperative consultation." In other words, the other doctors at the hospital should tell a knife-happy surgeon to stop doing surgery when there is no basis for it. It is this sixth definition of unnecessary surgery that most laymen and many physicians think of when they hear the term "unnecessary surgery." And while it can be a separate category, it can also be a subtle influence to bend the physician's judgment toward surgery in all the other categories as well. Fee-motivated surgery is both unprofessional and immoral. In an editorial in the *New England Journal of Medicine,* Dr. Frances Moore states, "Professional conduct might be defined as that in which the welfare of the patient always comes first." But fee-motivated surgery clearly puts the interests of the doctor first.

Two terms are often used in reference to questionable surgery: "unjustifiable" and "unnecessary." Sometimes they are used interchangeably, but this may confuse the issue. Perhaps we can clarify matters by defining and illustrating three types of surgery—or any type of medical care, for that matter.

One type of surgery is that which is both *necessary and justifiable.* For example, if a man has a visible skin tumor and a small biopsy reveals it to be malignant, then its surgical removal is justifiable in terms of the evidence for it, and necessary to prolong his life.

In contrast to this situation would be a case where surgery is both *unnecessary and unjustifiable.* For example, if a woman complains of indigestion and without further evidence a surgeon removes her uterus which turns out to be normal when inspected by a pathologist, then it was unnecessary as indicated by a lack of pathology. And it was unjustified in terms of the adequacy of the symptoms used as a basis for removing it. In this case the fee appears to be the only reason it was undertaken.

But much of what may be termed unnecessary surgery fits in the third type—the *unnecessary but justifiable.* This type of surgery may especially be undertaken with neurotic hypochondriacs, but is certainly not limited to that type of patient.

Suppose, Dr. William Nolen posits, that a patient with vague abdominal pain comes to him. Blood tests and x-rays reveal no explanation for the symptoms. He may operate "not because he thinks he's going to cure the patient but because he feels that the operation has to be done to rule in or rule out certain diseases." He may operate on the "remote chance that the pancreas is diseased," pointing out there is no way to x-ray it. He argues that if the pancreas turns out to be normal, as is usually the case in such instances, then the operation was unnecessary. That is, no disease was found. But he argues it was justifiable—"It had to be done so that we wouldn't miss a potentially curable disease."

The problem then is that retrospectively it is often possible to say an operation was unnecessary, but it is hard to say it was unjustifiable, because you lacked the evidence before the operation. Take appendectomies, for instance. Sometimes a child has some of the symptoms of the disease. But when operated on, a child may turn out to have a normal appendix. Nolen argues such surgery turned out to be unnecessary but not unjustifiable. "In fact," he says, "since the diagnosis of appendicitis can only be made with probability, not certainty, if a surgeon isn't removing one normal appendix in every ten cases he's probably not doing enough appendectomies. He's trying to be too certain, and probably letting some appendices go on to rupture." On the other hand, if 30 percent of the appendices he is removing are normal, then some of them may be unjustified, that is, lacking sufficient evidence to undertake them in the first place.

This lack of medical justification, he feels, can be attributed to either medical ignorance or greed. But the problem, in his words, is that "the unjustifiable surgery that's done can hardly ever be proved unjustifiable." This is where you run into the "matter of opinion" differences between physicians. A physician can almost always come up with some "reason" for undertaking surgery. Apparently what is needed is more explicit criteria for determining when an operation is likely to prove necessary.

Dr. Nolen feels that most unnecessary surgery is undertaken out of ignorance rather than greed, simply because he cannot understand doctors submitting patients to risk and suffering "for the sake of a few bucks." But then he goes on to admit that some surgery is economically motivated. He says:

When the layman reads about hospitals where, we'll say, the number of operations per unit of population done is 50 percent higher than the national average, he can't understand how the surgeons get away with it. I can. The surgeons in that hospital don't have enough legitimate work to keep them busy, so they loosen up on their standards. They start removing gall bladders that aren't diseased, on the off chance that doing it may get rid of the patient's indigestion. They take out a uterus because it may, possibly, relieve a backache. They open up the spine and look around, because "maybe there's a slipped disc, even if the x-rays don't show it." They lie to their patients and to themselves. They're operating for the money but won't admit it.

Dr. Nolen reports from his own experience of seeing unnecessary operations performed. For example, he tells of a physician who asked him to assist in a hernia operation on a boy complaining of pain after a football game. Nolen says that he had not examined the patient before the operation, but "After we'd cut down to the area where hernias lie, there was absolutely no evidence of a hernia." Then he goes on to explain that often hernias are "vague things"—muscular weakness in the abdominal wall where the surgeon can always put in a few stitches to tighten up the muscles, "even if the weakness exists only in the mind of the surgeon." Nolen says, "The surgery was unjustifiable because he [the surgeon] should have been able to tell preoperatively that there was no hernia. . . ."

Some elective procedures can be determined to be unnecessary postoperatively because the tissue which was removed was healthy instead of pathological. But many elective operations, like some hernias, involve no tissue removal, so it is nearly impossible to tell if they were unnecessary. "Doctors joke about 'acute remunerative appendicitis'; I suspect that acute remunerative hernia is a much more common disease," says Nolen.

Nolen believes that "most of the unjustifiable surgery that's done is relatively minor in nature," even though some would argue no surgery is minor in the sense of being without risk. He feels "the risk to the patient is negligible, and there's no chance of being caught." For operations like the removal of skin cysts, dilation and currettage, and hemorrhoidectomies, "a doctor is relatively safe when he's very liberal in advising these operations."

Sometimes patients or their families put pressure on doctors to operate. Dr. Nolen labels some of these "superneurotics." He tells of one patient with lipomas (fat blobs under the skin) who had been operated on twenty times in eight years to have these excised because she reported each time that she got better, even though they were in no way connected to her alleged back problem.

One group of patients that has been operated on more frequently in recent years is the elderly. Even since Medicare went into effect, doctors have been liberally operating on older people, many of them with terminal diseases for whom surgery holds little respite. Later in the book we will take a detailed look at one hospital in Massachusetts where a 51 percent mortality rate was reported among elderly patients undergoing open-heart operations. When this high rate of mortality was reported by the *Boston Globe*, the group of surgeons involved stopped doing the operation at one hospital.

While Nolen questions some of the reports on unnecessary surgery, he states: "But there is one group of patients who I know are sometimes unfairly and unjustifiably subjected to surgery. These are the patients with terminal diseases." As a surgeon, he says he can understand it. "Knife-happy surgeons are operating on people with extensive cancers, serious lung diseases and heart ailments that can't possibly be remedied; their rationalization is that 'If I don't operate he's certainly going to die—so I may as well operate even if there's only a one-in-a-million chance we can save him.'"

Unnecessary surgery exists. But, according to the distinctions I have adduced, it is a larger category than "unnecessary and unjustifiable" surgery. This is because a doctor can nearly always give some explanation of why he plans to undertake some surgery before he does it or why he did it after the operation is over. But we can still ask informed doctors, those who really know the medical literature, whether the justification was substantially convincing.

In making a charge that an operation was unnecessary, the second physician usually stands on surer ground in those kinds of operations where healthy tissue was removed but where diseased tissue would most fully have justified the operation. Still, the first physician can often make a claim, pre- or postoperatively, that some "suspicious" symptoms preceded what might be called an "exploratory operation." But in those types of operations where the removal of diseased tissue is not needed to prove the operation was necessary, we more directly confront the issue of differences of medical opinion. And we also may confront differences in lay opinion on what they may estimate to be a benefit. Perhaps on such issues where no explicit criteria exist, they need to be developed. Maybe the best general criterion that we can now come up with is "the weight of informed opinion" in a case-by-case study of the degree of necessity of each operation. Thus, the problems that exist in the first four types of "unnecessary surgery" are those of insufficiently explicit criteria.

Most of the studies of unnecessary surgery point to the kinds of surgery subsumable under categories 2 (surgery for removal of pathological tissue, but nonpathological is removed), 3 (where the helpfulness of the surgery is judged differently by doctors), 5 (outmoded or discredited surgery), and 6 (fee-induced surgery). And these categories are not mutually exclusive. In fact, two or more of these labels could be applied to the same operation.

As indicated earlier, there are variations in the degree of necessity—in medical, personal, and social terms. Is an operation on an eighty-year-old man with lung cancer necessary? If he has a 60 percent chance of surviving the surgery which might extend his life two years while subjecting him to considerable pain and a long recovery, would you recommend it if you were a surgeon? Would you elect to have it if you were that man?

On the other hand, would you recommend a hysterectomy to a thirty-five-year-old woman who has three children and whose mother died of cancer, simply because she was afraid of it but has no signs of it? As a subscriber to an insurance plan which would foot the $1,600 or $1,900 bill for it, do you object to the fact that hers and similar questionable cases will affect your future insurance premiums by 5 or 10 percent?

Before turning to the accumulating evidence of unnecessary surgery, we need to understand how surgery can act as a placebo—how it may make a patient feel better without really helping him in any other way.

4

SURGERY AS A PLACEBO

.Surgery as a placebo sounds like a contradiction; but it is not. That is because most people use only the limited definition of a placebo— a sugar pill or some other inert substance. That is one type, and perhaps the most common form placebos take. A second type of placebo is any active therapy that is unrelated to the condition for which it is given. For example, a hysterectomy could be a placebo for an irritable colon. A hysterectomy would certainly be an active therapy, but we would not expect it to have a specific effect for the irritable colon. Nor would we expect a small dose of digitalis (normally used for congestive heart failure) to be an appropriate treatment for the release of anxiety. Thus, an active placebo, unlike an inert placebo, may have some effect on a person physiologically. But it is still a placebo because it has no specific chemical, structural, or metabolic healing power for the illness being treated.

The placebo effect is different from the placebo. The placebo is the therapy given—whether an inert substance, an active drug, physical manipulation, surgery, radiotherapy, faith healing, or psychoanalysis— that by present knowledge is not related to healing the condition for which it is given. The placebo effect, in contrast, is the benign result which occurs as a result of any therapeutic intervention. The placebo effect is the altered perception, altered interpretation, or physiological change that stems from any therapeutic intervention, including both placebo therapies and nonplacebo therapies. Nonplacebo therapies involve an active therapy that is specifically related to the condition being treated.

Two words of caution are needed here, however. First, even so-called inert substances are not always inert. While sugar pills are inert for all intents and purposes, they might not be inert for a diabetic. Even water, if taken in sufficient quantities, may not be inert. Second, as we shall see later, what is in fact a placebo and what may be thought to be a placebo at any given time may be quite different. While some therapies were thought at a given time to be effective, they later turned out to be only placebos. On the other hand, it is possible that the use of what is thought to be an active placebo may turn out to be an active specific therapy as medical knowledge grows.

Dr. Arthur Shapiro has developed a comprehensive definition of a placebo that includes what we have termed inert substances and active procedures (nonspecific) unrelated to the condition for which they are given. His definition, in laymen's terms, is that a placebo is any therapy that is used to produce a nonspecific physical or psychological effect in the patient, but which, unknown to the patient and perhaps to the physician, is without specific activity for the condition being treated. This definition points out that for a placebo to be such, the patient must be unaware of the real nature of his treatment. On the other hand, the physician may intentionally use a placebo. Or he may be unaware that the therapy he is using is a placebo; he may think it is a specific active therapy.

Thus, any therapy, including surgery, can be a placebo if the use of it is not physiologically related to the process of healing or cure. For example, numerous studies have shown that sugar pills reduce pain by about half for one out of three people. In one study, around 30 percent of the patients received relief from postoperative pain with a placebo. In another study, 38 percent reported relief from angina pectoris (heart pain) when they took a placebo medication. Thirty-five percent got relief from the common cold when they took "dummy pills," 52 percent got relief from headaches, 40 percent from a cough, and 58 percent from seasickness. This is very fascinating, for it tells us a lot about medicine and medical care. As a general rule, we probably attribute more effectiveness to medical care than it deserves.

Let me explain the three possible reasons that people may get better when they are ill. The first reason is spontaneous change, or natural remission. Many illnesses are self-limiting. And the body has many built-in self-adjusting mechanisms to overcome infection or to make us rest with headaches or cramps or pain. Thus, given time, these self-curing healing processes often cure the dis-eases of the human body. The second process by which we can get better is the placebo process. Nobody is certain how it works, but there are several tentative explanations. One is that if a patient is led to believe that he will get better, his *expectations* and perhaps *interpretations* about future experiences of pain and discomfort may be changed. A doctor's prognostication that "you'll feel 100 percent better after you take this medicine" or have this surgery) may shift the focus of attention of the patient away from negative experiences to positive experiences or interpretations of them. Anxiety and mental stress may be reduced if a patient *believes* the positive predictions made on the side of a bottle of medicine or by a nurse or physician. Dr. H. K. Beecher, a famous Boston anesthetist, found that placebo effectiveness increased when patients were under greater as opposed to lesser stress.

Placebo processes may work in a second but not fully understood way. The new term for it is "biofeedback." Just as worrying (negative thought) may contribute to exhaustion, ulcers, hypertension, and coronary artery disease, so positive thought about the expected beneficial effects to come from a drug (actually a placebo) may in fact have beneficial physical effects. Thus, conscious or unconscious mental processes may effect bodily chemical changes in ways not yet fully understood. In fact, measurable objective changes in bodily processes have been produced by placebos, according to Dr. Beecher in an interesting article called "The Powerful Placebo." He points out that placebos have altered heartbeat and blood pressure, changed the gastric acidity level in patients, produced diarrhea, rashes, vomiting, and changes in the ratio of uric acid to creatinine adrenal cortical activity. Placebo processes, while they often have positive effects, are also negative in some of their outcomes. For 50 to 70 percent of patients given placebo therapy, there is no change; about 35 percent will report benefits, and about 10 percent will report negative effects from a placebo. To complicate the matter, there is no simple way to distinguish the curative effects of placebos independent of natural remission effects when both are present.

The third source of cure may be some medical intervention—a medicine, radiotherapy, physical therapy, surgery, or whatever. But nonplacebo therapeutic treatment does not mean the placebo effect is inactive. Any time a patient is under therapy, be it drug self-medication, the manipulations of a chiropractor, or the scalpel of a surgeon, he is subject to the changes in perception or physiological processes we have called the placebo effect. Thus, the placebo effect can occur whether the patient is undergoing placebo therapy unrelated to his condition or an "active" therapy deemed appropriate for his condition. This is why it is important to distinguish between a placebo and the placebo effect. A placebo is any therapy that is unrelated to the condition being treated. The placebo effect, on the other hand, is that change created by the process of undergoing any therapy, be it placebo or active therapy.

All this has a very important bearing on how a person interprets the effectiveness of the medical care he receives. If he is being exposed to therapy, he is very likely to attribute any changes experienced to the drug he took or the surgery he underwnt. But it is very possible that all or some parts of the gains he made were due to spontaneous natural remission or the powerful placebo effect. While he may thank his doctor or praise God, his body and his own mind may be just as responsible for the change.

Now, there are some ways to sort out how much gain in recovery from some episode of illness is due to either (1) active therapeutic intervention or (2) the effects of natural remission and the placebo effect taken singly or in combination.

To illustrate this, I would like to report on a piece of surgical research done earlier but which might be judged unethical by today's standards. In 1959 and 1960 two surgical research teams, working independently, evaluated a surgical procedure then quite popular and used for the relief of angina pectoris. The name of the operation was internal mammary-artery-ligation. These studies involved a double blind procedure. The first "blind" means that the patient doesn't know if he gets the real procedure or a placebo (in this case a sham operation). This "blind" technique enables the investigator to determine if there were any differences in results between those who got the real surgery and the placebo surgery. If the results, as measured by subjectively reported pain, reduced need for medication, and improved exercise tolerance, are the same for both groups, then the operation can be judged to be ineffective. The second blind means that those administering the placebo and the real therapy do not make the judgments of the effectiveness of the surgery. Instead, a third physician, who doesn't know which patients got the placebo surgery and which got the real surgery, makes these judgments to guard against the bias that the operating surgeons would have difficulty avoiding.

To illustrate this point about the biasing interpretation of the operating surgeon, Dr. Henry Beecher made a study of doctors "enthusiastic" about the effectiveness of the internal mammary-artery-ligation procedure for the relief of pain and those "skeptical" about it. He reports that "enthusiastic doctors" found 38 percent of their patients (71 of 188) obtained "complete relief of pain" from the operation. On the other hand, the doctors skeptical of its effectiveness found that only 10 percent of their patients (6 of 59) got complete relief from pain. This illustrates an important point about placebos made by Dr. S. Wolf. "The degree to which [the physician] is able to induce in his patients a state of arousal or readiness for a favorable response, the more potent the medication he gives will be. In other words, placebo effects are potent where there is strong motivation on the part of the patient toward recovery."

Now, how did these two research teams, headed respectively by a Dr. L. A. Cobb and Dr. E. G. Dimond, carry out their double blind evaluation of the effectiveness of the internal mammary-artery-ligation procedure? Patients were selected for the operation by precise criteria and randomly assigned to the group to be ligated or not ligated. They were told they were participating in an evaluation of the operation, but not told of the double-blind nature of the study or the use of a sham operation. All seventeen patients were seriously limited by angina. After they were taken to the operating room, the surgeon opened their chests and isolated the internal mammary artery. Then a random card was drawn which instructed the surgeon either to close the incision or ligate (tie off) the vessel and then close the incision. The surgical procedures were carried out in such a way that the cardiologist responsible for postoperative evaluation was unaware of which procedure was done. The cardiologist followed each patient postoperatively for anywhere from three to fifteen months.

The combined results of these two studies are informative. Twelve of the seventeen patients (or 70 percent) who had the sham procedure consisting only of a skin incision experienced subjective improvement. "Similar changes were noted in the group in which the internal mammary artery was ligated; hence this operation was judged to be of no value."

The study done by Cobb particularly showed the lack of effectiveness of the operation. In the ligated group 34 percent had a decrease in the use of nitroglycerin tablets to reduce pain, but 42 percent of those who had the sham procedure reduced their use of nitroglycerin tablets. Reports of subjective improvement by 32 percent of the ligated and 43 percent of the nonligated suggest little difference between the groups. Cobb reported that one patient who had the sham operation and "who had been unable to work because of his heart disease, was almost immediately rehabilitated and was able to return to his former occupation." Another patient, prior to the sham procedure, was able to walk on a treadmill for only four minutes before pain set in and his electrocardiogram became abnormal. After the placebo operation he was able to exercise ten minutes without pain and without electrocardiographic abnormality. Cobb and his associates concluded that "internal-mammary-artery-ligation probably has no effect on the pathophysiology of coronary-artery disease. The subjective benefit from this operation is more likely to be on a psychological basis, although any spontaneous improvement in collateral circulation cannot be excluded."

These three studies headed by Beecher, Cobb, and Dimond led to the demise of this procedure in about a two-year period. This fact points to the importance of surgical research using the double blind methodology to rule out bias in determining the effectiveness of surgical procedures, particularly new ones or those whose effectiveness is doubtful. As Dr. Beecher, a famed anesthesiologist, concludes, "One may question the moral or ethical right to continue with casual or unplanned new surgical procedures—procedures which may encompass no more than a placebo effect—when these procedures are costly of time and money and dangerous to health or life." But Dr. Beecher also says: "Our aim in medicine is to relieve often, and to cure when we can. Placebo effects are not to be despised; they play a part—sometimes a very important part—in surgical success; but we would be deceived by our own maneuvers if we failed to find out when placebo effects may be the sole agents functioning in a given case."

Thus, the placebo process is an important part of every healing process. Its effect will be more noticeable where the emotional stress associated with the illness is high. The magnitude of the placebo effect is also apparently higher when the physician is enthusiastic about the effectiveness of the treatment and this is conveyed to the patient. According to Dr. Arthur Shapiro, "The greater a physician's interest in a theory or therapy, particularly if it is his own innovation or if he is a recent convert, the more effective that therapy will appear to be . . . a greater intellectual and emotional investment is inherent in a physician using a new drug or treatment." Furthermore, he continues, "This may explain, in part, the reports of almost universal effectiveness accompanying the introduction of new therapies." Studies have shown that the effectiveness of a placebo may increase by as much as 100 percent when the *doctor* is told he is using an active agent and not a placebo.

Conversely, we would expect, but have no research evidence to confirm, that the placebo effect would be higher if the patient has a good rapport with his physician. And last, the evidence shows that about 35 percent of all patients experience improvement following either a placebo operation or a placebo medication. However, in these studies no attempt was made to distinguish the placebo process from any natural remission that might be occurring.

The extent to which the "success" of American medicine is misattributed to therapeutic interventions is unknown. Patients who are being treated are often unaware that the subsidence of their illnesses may be due to either natural remission or the placebo effect while they attribute it to therapy. Furthermore, doctors can be as subject to the placebo effect as patients. They may believe that the therapy they are administering is the real healing agent if their patient gets better, even though it may be totally or relatively ineffective. Not only may the doctor be the conveyor of the placebo effect, he too may be captured by it as a result of his own enthusiasm. Dr. Beecher tells of another study that compared patient results from a gastroenterostomy procedure to treat duodenal ulcers. "Enthusiastic doctors" *found* an 82 percent cure rate compared to only 47 percent for "skeptical doctors." Furthermore, the enthusiastic doctors reported only 2 percent of their patients having a return of "marginal" ulcer problems in contrast to 34 percent of the patients being treated by the skeptical doctors. Both the patient and the doctor, and either the patient or the doctor, can come under the sway of the placebo effect. "The observation that surgery can evoke a placebo effect of great magnitude should be no more startling than the demonstrated fact that the indisputably effective action of morphine on pathological pain is, on the avergae, only twice that of a placebo," according to Dr. Beecher.

Much surgery has, of course, a better average record of effectiveness than that of a placebo (for example, drainage of an abscess, extirpation of an inflamed appendix), . . . yet, even in the correction of such plainly "objective" situations as these, it probably would be a mistake to underrate the usefulness of a favorable placebo component in the restoration of the patient to health.

Perhaps Galen was on target in the second century when he observed, "He cures most in whom most are confident."

In his book *Surgeon under the Knife* Dr. William Nolen reviews about four different surgical procedures, all now outmoded, which have been used to try to relieve a patient with heart pain (angina). They included the internal mammary-artery-ligation operation, thyroidectomies (to slow the body's metabolism), sympathectomies (cutting the nerves which relay heart pain to the brain), and even sprinkling talcum powder on the open heart in the hope that this irritation would stimulate the growth of additional blood bessels. He comments, "In 1975 we know that none of these operations were really any good. Admittedly, about 30 percent of patients swore they were 'better' after their operation, whichever one it might have been. But," he concludes, "30 percent of patients will think they are improved, no matter what you do to them." This is what we have called the placebo effect. As Nolen points out, "Convince patients that something will reduce their symptoms and in patients susceptible to suggestion, the symptoms will be relieved or ignored. Surgery can be used as a placebo just as sugar pills are."

Two forces are at work in the medical profession which tend to over-magnify its successes and undoubtedly contribute to the overutilization of medical care services by both patients and physicians. The first of these forces is the "medical decision rule." This rule is that it is better to impute or diagnose disease than to risk its being overlooked or denied. To fail to look for disease even when it is absent could lead to greater jeopardy to the patient's health than to "find" it when it is absent. Contrary to legal theory and practice, where it is better to let a guilty man go free than to convict an innocent man, medical theory and practice generally operates on the converse principle that it is better to treat a healthy person than to diagnose a sick person as healthy. And the role of the demands and desires of patients who come to doctors to present their complaints cannot be discounted.

Two pieces of research support this medical decision rule where doctors are biased toward finding sickness rather than health. The first was a study done on the advisability of children having a tonsillectomy, when this surgery was at the height of its popularity in the 1930s. In this study of 1,000 school children, 611 had already had their tonsils removed. The remaining 389 were reviewed by a group of second physicians who selected 44 percent of them (174) for a tonsillectomy. The remaining group of 215 "normal tonsil" children was reviewed by a third group of physicians, who found 99 (46 percent) of them in need of a tonsillectomy. Still a fourth group of doctors examined the remaining group of 116 children and found nearly half of them in need of a tonsillectomy. As Eliot Freidson comments on this case, "Since it is very unlikely that each group of physicians would overlook the severity of signs in fully one-fourth of the cases it saw, it seems more plausible to conclude that each used a sliding scale of severity rather than an absolute criterion." Another illustration of the bias toward finding disease is the ratio of findings of "false positives" (diagnosed as ill but later found to be healthy) to "false negatives" (diagnosed as healthy but later found to be ill). In a review of 14,867 x-ray films for tuberculosis, physicians made 1,216 false positive diagnoses compared to only 24 false negatives. Thus, in this study, for every time a sick patient was judged healthy there were 50 times when a healthy patient was judged sick. As I have written elsewhere:

Overdiagnosis, overmedication, and overtreatment are more likely where (1) financial or other benefits accrue to those who locate illness, (2) the doctor wants to appear to be doing something helpful even though the patient's reports of illness are not accompanied by clear or unambiguous signs of illness, and (3) there are popular or conventional diagnoses and treatments, including placebos, which might help. Thus, doctors are not only likely to take illness more seriously than laymen, they are more likely to detect signs for it no matter how vague they are and to initiate treatment even though natural processes may be the curing agent.

The second force at work in the medical profession which tends to overmagnify its successes and support continuing treatment that is questionable is the "clinical mentality of doctors." This is the biased attribution of success to the wrong element, themselves, rather than the placebo effect or natural remission. Of course, physicians believe in the therapy they give, and undoubtedly it is often helpful. But the placebo effect can accompany placebo treatments, treatments that are believed to be objectively effective but are only placebos, and treatments that are objectively effective. In seeking help a patient usually believes the doctor can help him; and in giving it the doctor usually believes he is doing something that will help him. But the expectation that one will benefit from the encounter may influence both the outcome and the perception and interpretation of the outcome. Furthermore, the physician's diagnosis and labeling of some signs and symptoms as illness and his prediction and interpretation of progress to the patient influence the patient to look for progress. In the process the patient has adopted the physician's clinical frame of reference—that is, a bias toward finding his intervention to be the curative agent.

Because psychosomatic elements are present in so many illnesses, we need to understand that some human problems never exist in a physiological sense and that some have their origin and cure in mental processes intricately related to physiological processes. Thus, some doctors are judged good because the most important thing they did was to be there and to furnish optimistic prognostications. Furthermore, since each physician develops his own theories of illness based in part on his own unique clinical experiences, he may attract patients who believe in him, and report on those cases which appear successful. While this may be neither systematic nor scientific, it may be helpful to patients and rewarding to the doctor because of the intellectual, emotional, and financial investment he has in his own theory and practice.

A critical distinction must be made between surgery that is only a placebo but unknown as such to the surgeon and the intentional use of surgery as a placebo by the surgeon. The mammary-artery-ligation procedure was a placebo, but at first was believed to be an operation effective in bringing additional blood to the heart through collateral channels surrounding the heart. However, because there was doubt about its effectiveness, it was subjected to testing by the double blind technique. This proved its effectiveness was about the same as a sham operation, so it was dropped because objective data did not substantiate it as an effective operation. But how many operations are there whose effectiveness is due only to a placebo effect? The answer is, we do not know. To find the answer, carefully designed surgical research is needed.

On the other side of the coin is the question of how many operations are undertaken which use surgery solely for its placebo effect. This question will remain unanswered because we lack the information to answer it. But there is evidence that many placebo medications are given.

Dr. Sissela Bok has reported that "thorough studies have estimated that as many as 35 to 45 percent of all prescriptions are for substances that are incapable of having an effect on the condition for which they are prescribed." In other words, they are placebos. One study of prescriptions for the common cold, she reports, revealed that 59 percent were placebos.

The intentional use of placebos raises a number of ethical questions.

Is it ethical to use sham medications or operations? Some would say yes because they see it as a way for the physician to perform his function—to heal people. "If the doctor gets the job done, what does it matter how he gets it done?" they ask. Furthermore, they would argue, it can be used as a diagnostic tool to determine, in some cases, the nature and source of a patient's illness. Most placebos are cheap and harmless, but this cannot be said for placebo surgery.

But some feel that the use of placebos is a deceitful practice. The patient is kept uninformed about the suspected nature of his illness. And the doctor is not giving patients their right to informed consent. Furthermore, they are involved in needless care and expense, and most patients will not improve and a few will get worse with placebos. Sometimes, as in the inappropriate use of antibiotics, patients may be exposed to needless risks such as drug reactions or the weakening of natural immunities. Furthermore, such secret medications may be used to mask the physician's ignorance or his hurried practice, or to persuade the patient that the doctor is doing something helpful (which, in a placebo sense, he may be doing.)

Placebos may be used more than most people think. In a small and nonrandom survey of physicians by Dr. Arthur Shapiro and Dr. Elmer Struening, doctors estimated on the average that they intentionally gave their own patients placebos 14.1 percent of the time. But they estimated that 20.9 percent of other doctors did so. When they were asked what percentage of patients were unintentionally treated with placebos (that is, the doctors were using placebos but were unaware that they were such), doctors estimated that 20.3 percent of their own patients and 31.2 percent of the patients of other doctors were given placebos. Over 68 percent of the 191 reporting physicians thought other physicians were more likely to use them than they were themselves. (Surgeons reported the least use of placebos, followed by psychoanalysts.) Shapiro and Struening interpreted this as a defensive attitude toward the use of placebos. That is, most doctors were more likely to think other doctors were using placebos than that they were themselves.

In most instances, we might imagine that any surgical procedure that is either clearly a placebo or a borderline case of it, is deliberately administered as such. Doctors are the ones who know most about surgery and advise patients on the need for it. Take tonsillectomy, for instance; 20 to 30 percent of the children in most communities have one, according to Dr. Robert Bolande. But a review of the medical literature by Dr.

Bolande and by Dr. H. E. Evans found that only 2 to 3 percent of all children need it. There appears to be no long-term benefit from having the operation. A few children from about ages four to six may derive short-term benefits from it if they are plagued by severe and recurrent tonsilitis. While it is a minor operation, according to Dr. Bolande, about 1 child in 1,000 will die from it, and about 15 in 1,000 get serious complications from it.

Then why is it performed so often, even though the rate of it has been declining as its necessity is questioned in both medical and lay circles? According to Dr. Bolande, it is one form of "ritualistic surgery." It is performed not only for profit but as a standardized procedure that is too frequently unquestioned by either parents or doctors. Parents often want the operation for their children. As children they had the operation. In Bolande's words, "Physicians' willingness to comply with parental demand has institutionalized, and indeed ritualized, the operation to a considerable extent." He argues that this particular surgery not only reflects ability to pay but the social status and needs of the parents. Perhaps we could conceive of some children's tonsillectomies as placebos for worried parents. It may make them feel better than the children, for whom it may also act as a placebo.

How much surgery is done ritualistically today? How much of this ritualistic surgery is primarily a placebo or only a placebo? These are important questions. But only doctors have the answer to these questions. Sometimes.

Dr. F. J. Ingelfinger, a recent editor of the *New England Journal of Medicine,* helps give perspective to the role of medicine in dealing with man's illnesses. He points out that some illnesses are caused by doctors. These iatrogenic illnesses are usually caused inadvertently but are still traceable to medical intervention. In an editorial entitled "Health: A Matter of Statistics or Feeling," he argues that health statistics do not reflect much of what doctors do.

Let us assume that 80 percent of patients have either self-limited disorders or conditions not improvable, even by modern medicine. In slightly over 10 percent of the cases, however, medical intervention is dramatically successful. . . . But, alas, the final 9 percent, give or take a point or two, the doctor may diagnose or treat inadequately, or he may just have bad luck. Whatever the reason, the patient ends up with iatrogenic problems. So the balance of accounts ends up marginally on the positive side of zero.

In this chapter I have looked at the role the powerful placebo plays in healing and in medicine in general. The placebo effect has been defined as any cure or change the patient experiences that is due to the fact that he was undergoing therapy and in contact with a healer but not due to the healing agent in and of itself. Thus, the placebo effect can occur in any treatment process whether the treatment was itself a placebo or not. We have also pointed out that while some treatments are known to be effective and others only a placebo, still others fall in a gray area of scientifically unknown effectiveness. That is, the curing that occurs with their use, as in the case of the internal mammary-artery-ligation surgery before its scientific study, may be due to either the placebo effect or its medical efficacy. This raises the possibility that some current therapies, including surgery, may be no more than a placebo. This creates the situation where physicians could be unwittingly using placebo therapies. All this means that sometimes surgery could be undertaken where it is known to be ineffective but used purely for its placebo effect or undertaken believing it is effective when in fact it is only a placebo.

In this chapter I have also pointed out that any cure a patient experiences may be traceable to one of three factors taken singly or in combination: effective therapy, spontaneous remission, or the placebo effect. Because most clinical practice of medicine is not designed to ferret out how much of the healing that occurs is traceable to each of these factors, there may be considerable misattribution of the healing power of medical care. This, I have argued is due to two factors. The first is the medical decision rule wherein doctors detect more medical illness that needs treatment than may be warranted. Then they may misattribute cures that occur to their own therapeutic efforts rather than to the spontaneous remission or the placebo effect which are the real causes. I have argued that such a situation suggests we need not only be aware of the significant moral problems that the intentional use of placebos raises but also the need for more rigorous medical care research to determine how much treatment involves no more than placebo effects.

5

HOW MUCH UNNECESSARY SURGERY?
RETROSPECTIVE EVIDENCE

There is no doubt in anyone's mind that some unnecessary surgery is being performed. But how much of it is unnecessary? Physicians, journalists, and public health specialists often talk of overutilization and underutilization. And it is possible to have some of both at the same time. There may be totally unnecessary operations and those that are borderline in terms of improving patient welfare. That is overutilization. But while that is occurring there may simultaneously be those who need and/or could benefit from surgery but whose needs remain undetected through lack of adequate medical care or because of financial or even psychological barriers—fear of death or of poor outcomes.

How do we find out how much surgery is unnecessary? This leads us into two separate but, unfortunately, related areas. One is the scientific question of what is *acceptable evidence* of unnecessary surgery. Is the information obtained in such a way that it is reliable (accurately recorded) and valid (truly representative of what is happening in the world of surgery)? The other area is that of the politics of surgery. Here we find that not only what is said is important, but who says it is equally important. Thus, we enter the area of ideology. Vested interests begin to show. Fee surgeons differ with salaried surgeons over the role of fees and salaries in inducing or reducing surgery.

Dr. William Nolen, once a salaried resident at Bellevue Hospital, a public institution, tells an interesting story of when he went to North Shore University Hospital, a not-for-profit teaching affiliate of the Cornell University Medical College.

North Shore gave me many lessons in the business of surgery. Some of them were distasteful. I learned, for example, that every surgeon wasn't always honest. It came as a kind of shock to me. At Bellevue, and at Triboro, we never thought about money. Whether we did a hemorrhoid or a stomach resection, the pay was the same. Not so in private practice. The insurance companies and the patients paid a lot more for a big case than they did for a small one. And it influenced what some of these men did, or said they did.

To illustrate his point, he told of a couple of cases at this hospital. One morning, he reports, he scrubbed for a lung case with a Dr. Small (fictitious name).

We opened the chest and found that the cancer was widespread. Resection was impossible.

"Hopeless, I'm afraid," Small said. "Can't get it out." I thought he'd close right up, but no—first he resected a small segment of lung.

"Why are you taking out that piece, Dr. Small?" I asked. "That certainly isn't going to help the patient."

He laughed. "Something for the pathologist, Nolen. Insurance companies pay better for lung resections than they do for in-and-out cases. We've got to be able to show some lung tissue. Don't worry. I won't hurt Mr. Francis any." It didn't, but that hardly justified the procedure.

Nolen tells of another occasion at the same hospital. A patient came in with bowel obstruction due to widespread cancer. "The man was obviously terminal and any operation was bound to be futile," reports Nolen. "I knew it and so did Dr. David Lund (a fictitious name), whose patient he was." Nolen said he "couldn't believe it" when Lund had the man put on the surgery schedule. Nolen continues:

"Gee, Dr. Lund, do you really think it's necessary? I can feel tumor all over his abdomen." I knew I was sticking my neck out, but I had decided to chance it.

"Look, Nolen," he said angrily, "you haven't been around long enough to start advising me. If there's a thousand-to-one chance we can help this man, it's worth taking."

I didn't bother arguing. So we opened, could do nothing, and closed. The patient died the next day. The whole case took forty-five minutes. Lund charged the family three hundred dollars. The bastard.

Doctors also differ over the need for surgery. Unlike internists and family physicians who can sit around and ponder what medication is best for the patient, the surgeon is a man of action. He cannot try one drug for a while and if that doesn't work, try another. He decides to operate or not. In the words of a surgeon, "Surgery attracts a different sort of person than does medicine. The guy that goes into surgery is the fellow who doesn't want to sit around waiting for results. He wants the quick cure of a scalpel, not the slow cure of a pill. . . . What he lacks in patience he makes up for in decisiveness." And this is one thing that apparently attracts surgeons into surgery. As Dr. Nolen writes in *A Surgeon's World*, "I admired the decisiveness of the surgeon who would· see a kid with a belly ache, say 'Let's open him up,' and get the job done." In fact, surgeons often see themselves as the complete doctor because they use both pills and the knife. "The general surgeon was king of the mountain. He treated the whole patient with all the tools that were available; other doctors needed his help but he could usually get along without theirs." Understandably, then, surgeons have a bias toward finding surgery necessary.

Other people differ over the amount of unnecessary surgery. Some patients put their surgeon along with other physicians on a pedestal. They would never question his judgment about the need for surgery. But some patients have become more questioning and critical in the light of malpractice suits. And there are politicians who want to gain publicity yardage from reporting on unnecessary surgery. And in response, doctors say that such reports on the extent of unnecessary surgery are exaggerated. They understandably want to protect their autonomy in setting fees and making medical judgments.

Because of these many differences of opinion, we may never know with much exactness how much unnecessary surgery there is. While we often conceive of medicine as a science, it is an art as much. It is an art where rapport with the patient and the complex judgment of whether surgery will help the patient are not reducible to a neat scientific formula. There are often unexpected outcomes from surgery because people are idiosyncratic. As Dr. Robert Brown said to me, "People are biological systems, not mathematical systems. What works with one patient may not work with another."

While acknowledging that any exact determination of the amount of unnecessary surgery is impossible, we still want to look at some of the evidence. Before we look at the evidence itself, we need to look at the forms in which it can be collected. A surgical detective knows that some evidence is better than other evidence. Circumstantial evidence is different from case-by-case evidence.

One general form of evidence is that reported in retrospective studies. In retrospective studies some person other than the performing surgeon looks at the clinical evidence on a case-by-case basis and makes a determination of whether the operation was necessary *after* the surgery is performed. In some cases the records are not complete. Furthermore, the criteria by which either the performing surgeon or the review surgeon makes a decision are not always spelled out. Often there are differences about the relative effectiveness and safety of many surgical procedures. And if there are two different surgeons, one with good success with an operation and another with "fair" success, we can understand these differences. Hindsight evidence, such as whether the removed tissue was pathological, does not necessarily add to future foresight unless the usable information is distilled out for future use. We shall look at a number of retrospective studies.

A second general form of evidence involves what are usually called utilization studies. In this type the rate of surgery for group 1 is compared to the rate of surgery for group 2. Such studies may be done with considerable scientific rigor or with little. For example, to see if more surgery is done in group 1, which uses fee surgeons, than in group 2, which uses salaried surgeons, we might compare the *rate* at which group 1 and 2 patients are hospitalized or have surgery performed on them or have particular types of surgical procedures done. But such studies, while suggestive, can have greater rigor added to them if the data they use is "standardized." By that we mean that the researchers have controlled for or equalized the two groups in those areas that might affect the amount of surgery done on them. Such things as the age, sex, socioeconomic status, years of education, type of occupation, and region of the country, may influence how much illness people get. While the more rigorous studies include or standardize as many of these variables as possible, it is impossible to include everything. Finding a person in group 1 who is identical in every way to a person in group 2 is a scientific impossibility if individuality means anything. Nevertheless, the better types of statistical studies try to control for or standardize those variables which may have a major influence on the incidence of illness and thereby the surgical remedy for it.

A third type of study related to unnecessary surgery is *concurrent second and third opinion studies.* Some of these are fairly simple, but others are more complex and have greater rigor. In second opinion studies, if the first surgeon recommends surgery the patients get an opinion from another surgeon, or even a third opinion. But here there are lots of subtle variations about the details of added opinions that could be important. One important variation is who selects the second surgeon. If the first surgeon selects him, both may be biased in the same direction. If the patient or insurance company selects him, there could be less bias. Another is whether the patient *may* (voluntary) or *must* (involuntary— demanded by the insurance company or someone else) get the second opinion. The involuntary plan would be more scientifically rigorous because it eliminates the bias due to the "self-selection" of those who get the second opinion. A second variation would be to study whether patients undergo the operation if the second surgeon advises against it. And who does the surgery, the first or second surgeon, or neither? And then, to be even more rigorous, we would need to study the patients over time to determine if those who went without surgery subsequently got it and how they fared with or without it. Did the patients who got surgery fare better or worse than the patients who did not when they got the same set of opinions—two doctors for it or one for and one against it. Furthermore, such studies, to get even more rigorous, would need to standardize the study procedures so that relatively equivalent persons with the same disorder were being compared. Needless to say, such studies are time consuming and costly to carry out.

Each of these three types of studies—retrospective case studies, retrospective utilization studies, and prospective or concurrent second opinion studies—may be well or poorly done. And, as we shall see later, there are a number of variations on them. Some will be explicit in the criteria they use to determine necessity while others will not. Some involve small samples at one hospital or in one limited geographic area while others use larger samples. Some compare rates of surgery between groups whose degree of similarity is unknown while others try to compare groups which are similar or whose variations in sex, age, severity of illness, and the like are statistically standardized to make them comparable. Thus, the quality of the study is important in determining how far we can rely on it.

Most of the early evidence of unnecessary surgery, gathered in the 1940s, 1950s, and the early 1960s, was relatively limited in scope. Most of it came in the form of retrospective case studies—and many of these were case studies of one or more hospitals. However, some came in the form of malpractice cases, a few of which are cited in the second chapter of this book. Nevertheless, they suggest that the problem of unnecessary surgery has been around for some time and is sizable.

In 1948 Dr. James C. Doyle surveyed the medical records on 6,248 hysterectomy operations performed in thirty-five Los Angeles area hospitals. He found 12.5 percent of these operations unnecessary and another 24 percent deserving "more conservative treatment." Thirty percent of the women operated on were between the ages of twenty and twenty-nine. The operation barred them from future childbearing. Perhaps not surprising, but nevertheless highly revealing, is the fact that hospitals varied greatly in their rates of questionable uterine surgery, from an acceptable 5 percent to an incredible 84 percent.

Although Dr. Doyle surveyed operations in 1948, his report was not published until 1953. In the prior year Dr. Paul Lembcke did a retrospective utilization study of primary appendectomy rates in twenty-three hospital service areas. (A primary appendectomy occurs when only the appendix is removed; a secondary appendectomy occurs when it is removed in the process of doing another operation.) The findings, he concluded, "indicate that considerably more operations of this type are done than are necessary in light of our present knowledge—excesses of from 25 to 100 percent in various areas." He pointed out that a lower incidence of appendectomies was unrelated to a higher death rate from appendicitis. He also found that appendectomy rates were lower in teaching hospitals and that some of the cases he surveyed could have been treated more conservatively by antibiotics.

One hospital and two of its surgeons came under his fire when he "found that among sixteen physicians with surgical privileges, one half of the primary appendectomies were done by two, neither of whom received referred cases; and that clear-cut indications for surgical operation were lacking in a large proportion of patients operated on by the two physicians."

In 1954 Dr. Henry Weinert addressed an AMA public relations conference on how the use of a tissue committee, to inspect surgically removed tissue for signs of pathology, cut down on some questionable surgery. Before the committee went into operation at St. Mary's Hospital in Passaic, New Jersey, appendectomies made up 28 percent of the total number of surgical cases, of which one-fifth were found to have no or minimal pathology. After the tissue committee began auditing removed tissue, appendectomies dropped to 8 to 9 percent of the surgical workload, with only 5 percent of them showing no signs of pathology. And a lack of pathological tissue in "emergency" operations rapidly dropped from 29 percent before the audit to 10 percent after it.

One of the areas that have been studied for years is the number of questionable "female" operations. A 1954–59 survey of five hospitals showed that the removal of uteri from females was justified between 41 percent and 88 percent of the time, with a typical rate of justified surgery being around 60 to 65 percent. Dr. Lembcke in another study of 105 hospitals judged that one-third of the hysterectomies were unjustified. Drs. Stephenson and Meyers in a study of 7 hospitals found that the rate of unjustified hysterectomies varied from 0 to 32 percent, while questionable appendectomies ranged from 3 to 41 percent in 8 hospitals.

At about the same time that tissue committees were being initiated in many hospitals, so were medical audits. A medical audit is defined as "the evaluation of medical care in retrospect through analysis of clinical records." Scientific medical audits involve, according to Dr. Lembcke, uniform definition of treatments and diagnoses, the verification of clinical records by written or laboratory reports, a determination of the accuracy of clinical records, the determination of the results of care or surgery by objective criteria, and the comparison of the quality of care either before and after the auditing is begun or with a "control" hospital where no auditing is done. The purpose of such auditing is to make certain that the full benefits of medical knowledge are brought to the care of each patient and to ensure the necessity and appropriateness of surgical and medical care.

To show that medical auditing can change the quality of care in a hospital, Dr. Lembcke did one in a San Francisco hospital. In two thirteen-week periods before the audit began, Lembcke found that only 29 percent and 33 percent of the surgery was appropriate or justified for the condition being treated. After the auditing process had been in operation for half a year, two thirteen-week audits were again conducted. This time he found 89 percent and 91 percent of the operations either appropriate or justified. The number of operations declined from an average of 230 before the audit to 130 after the audit, a drop of 43 percent. Hospital mortality dropped from 2 percent to 1.1 percent, hysterectomies declined by 43 percent; major operations in this one hospital dropped by 600 in one year. And the number of surgeons who were doing appropriate and justified surgery at a 70 percent rate climbed from 5 out of 26 to 21 out of 26.

In 1957 Dr. Paul Hawley, director of the American College of Surgeons, created waves in the medical profession when he claimed unnecessary operations were widespread and were not limited to just a few unethical doctors as AMA leaders had contended. Hawley estimated that 90 percent of all surgical uterine suspensions were unnecessary, that 60 percent of the appendectomies of some "operators" were unjustified, and that Caesarean births ran as high as 15 percent in some hospitals when the normal rate was about 3 percent.

Dr. Hawley made his comments at a time when tissue committees were being initiated in many hospitals to meet the accreditation standards of the Joint Commission on Accreditation of Hospitals. Hawley said, "After accreditation by the commission, one hospital's surgery rates, with the same patient load, fell from 769 operations in one year to 298; from 305 appendectomies to 66; from 30 Caesareans in 555 births to one Caesarean in 652 births."

In 1966 Martin Gross published his well-researched book entitled *The Doctors*. In it he questioned the quality of much of America's medical care. He looked at a number of studies on the prevalence of unjustified surgical procedures. A study of 1,002 appendectomies in five Balitmore hospitals showed 21 percent clearly unnecessary and another 28 doubtful. Of course, there is considerable variation by state and locale, and by quality of hospitals, he pointed out. One Michigan study found justified appendectomies ranged from a high of 93.6 percent to a low of 52.1 percent. One physician was discovered who was apparently running an appendectomy mill: 73 percent of the patients under his knife were found to have normal appendices. Gross also reported on a long-term gynecological survey that covered five nonteaching hospitals in three southern states over a four year period. This study found 56 percent of the gynecological procedures either unnecessary or doubtful, with 83 percent of the resection of ovaries believed unjustified.

Martin Gross was one of the first researchers to make a national estimate of the amount of unnecessary surgery. In 1966 he estimated 2 million such operations are performed yearly. This figure is comparable to the figure of 2.38 million in 1974 that the House subcommittee came up with. But the story is much more personal and tragic than these large numbers might indicate. Several thousand, maybe ten or twelve thousand, people will die from the surgery; others will be seriously impaired. Gross estimated that of 410,000 appendectomies done annually, 100,000 are unneeded and perhaps 500 patients would die as a result of the risks inherent in anesthesia, postoperative surgical infection, and other complications.

Take the real case of a man we shall call Martin Cromwell. His feet occasionally hurt him, but he could carry on a normal life. During one period of discomfort he went to the outpatient clinic of a hospital. The doctor he saw there strongly suggested he have surgery.

After the patient confessed that he was "scared stiff of the knife" and that he had never had an operation before, the doctor assured him it was only a "very minor operation." The doctor continued, "It requires only a small incision in your back and the clipping of a nerve. You'll be in the operating room only forty to forty-five minutes."

So, persuaded, Cromwell entered the hospital for an operation called a lumbar sympathectomy, which entails cutting a nerve in the sympathetic nervous system. Once the nerve is cut, the muscles in his legs would presumably relax and allow the surrounding blood vessels in his legs to expand. With increased blood flow to his feet and legs, the pain should be reduced.

The physician who examined and operated on Cromwell was an assistant resident in training. We shall call him Dr. Harris. The only other physicians present when he operated were two interns. Unfortunately for Cromwell that day, a foremost specialist in sympathetic nerve system surgery who was on the hospital's staff was gone.

When Cromwell consented to the surgery, he understood it to involve an inch long incision in the back. Dr. Harris approached the nerve the opposite way, through an eight-inch opening in his stomach. After lifting out his internal organs, Harris set about removing the entire nerve chain instead of simply clipping the nerve. With an unsteady hand the insufficiently experienced resident snapped the nerve chain after partially severing it with a scalpel. It disappeared in the abdominal cavity. In the process of probing for the nerve lost somewhere under the large artery and vein which carry blood to and from the legs, Harris punctured the vein, flooding the abdominal cavity with blood. In trying to get at the punctured vein which was enmeshed in fibrous tissue, he punctured it several more times. He was in trouble. Now he cut into the thigh near the groin so that he could trace the vein and tie it off. He did that, but the blood kept flowing uncontrolled. The artery had also been accidentally perforated in his search for the nerve chain.

The forty-five-minute operation was turning into a nightmare. Harris sent for help, because with the great loss of blood Cromwell's condition became "critical." The hospital's surgical chief rushed to the hospital. He abandoned efforts to repair the punctured artery and vein. He tied off the blood vessels in an effort to save Cromwell's life. When he awoke that night, Cromwell discovered the sad truth: he was paralyzed from the waist down.

With the major vein and artery to his left leg tied off, only a limited supply of blood could get to that leg. Gangrene set in. To save his life his left leg was amputated below the knee. But the amputation was defective, so he had to undergo a second amputation above the knee. Soon after his reamputation he suffered a heart attack. A blood clot moved to his right leg, where it obstructed circulation. Gangrene set in, necessitating the amputation of his right leg.

During the first operation Cromwell spent seven and a half hours in the operating room, where he needed seventeen pints of blood. When he left the hospital over four months later, he had lost eighty-six pounds, had stumps for legs, a severely impaired heart, and was susceptible to narcotic readdiction because of its extended use to relieve his pain.

Howard and Martha Lewis comment on this case:

> If any person were so assaulted on the street instead of in an operating room, the person who crippled him would probably be sent up for life. But there is a further irony: Martin Cromwell very likely should not have been operated on at all.
>
> His hospital record shows that his condition had never been diagnosed. Speculation as to what troubled him ranged from hardening of the arteries to Buerger's disease, an ailment resulting from excessive smoking. If any disease were present, it was in its early stages. Except for isolated periods of discomfort, Cromwell could walk and work without distress. Nonsurgical treatment ordinarily would have been tried before surgery was ever considered.
>
> But chances are Cromwell would never have needed an operation. As his medical history shows, he suffered one particular condition that in all likelihood accounted for much of the pain in his feet. Though obvious, it was evidently overlooked. He had fallen arches.

Rarely does surgery, necessary or not, turn out with such horrible results. But it does happen. Every day in the United States 50,000 people are operated on. About 700 of these will die on the operating table or thereafter as a result of the surgery. (This assumes a mortality rate of 1.4 percent for all operations; it is lower, maybe .5 percent, for discretionary operations.) Many others will be hurt or damaged from surgery, but too little is known about surgical morbidity. While it is true that some of these people would have died shortly without the surgery or would have had their lives impaired, surgery always carries risks, and it ought to be undertaken only where there is a clear need for it.

6

MORE EVIDENCE AND THE
SEARCH FOR CAUSES

In the last chapter we looked at a number of retrospective case studies and utilization studies. They pointed to a sizable amount of unnecessary surgery being performed.

In the decade from 1966 to 1975, the study of unnecessary surgery took two new turns. One twist was a series of studies comparing variations in the rate of surgery between two different groups. The groups that were compared differed in terms of the relative availability of surgeons in an area, hospital beds available, nationality, insurance coverage, and how surgeons were paid—salaries versus fees. This turn allowed the second turn—the making of inferences about *why* rates of surgery differed between groups. Was it due to differences in the way surgeons are trained in the United States compared to the United Kingdom? Was it due to variations in the local availability of surgeons in comparison to internists and other specialists who don't practice surgery? Are there variations in surgery by the amount and kind of insurance coverage, the socioeconomic class of patients?

These studies, then, in contrast to most of those cited in the last chapter, while still concerned with the rate and amount of questionable surgery, sought to develop some *theories* of why there are sizable variations from one group to another group. Furthermore, over time most of these studies have become more rigorous in their design. This allows us to trust their conclusions more.

One of the first studies of this type was carried out by Charles Lewis, an M.D., by analyzing records of the Kansas Blue Cross Association in

1965. A computer mapping system divided the state into ten regions so that each of the regions was similar along some thirty-six variables such as labor force, population density, age distribution, per capita income, and soil and water distribution. Dr. Lewis then determined the rate per 10,000 people for two "nonelective" procedures and four "elective" surgical procedures in each of the ten areas. These procedures constituted about 23 percent of the operations performed that year. The statewide average for one of the so-called nonelective procedures, appendectomy, was 23.7 operations per 10,000, but this went from a low of 14.6 to a high of 61.8. In other words, the rate of appendectomies in one region (each region was composed of from eight to eleven counties) was over two and a half times the state average and over four times as high as the rate in the lowest county. And this was for a so-called emergency operation which was assumed to be distributed rather randomly over the population.

But wait. Maybe people were going outside their region of residence to be operated on. He checked this, but found "that over 80 percent of the patients hospitalized in institutions in any region came from counties in that region." Furthermore, "There was little variation among regions in terms of the percentage of 'nonregional' patients." Thus, he rejected this explanation of why there were such wide variations among the regions.

The other nonelective procedure was cholecystectomy—gallbladder removal. The statewide average per 10,000 patients for this was 27.0, but operations varied from a low of 12.1 to 42.3. While the variation was not as high as for appendectomies, the highest region had a rate three and one-half times that of the lowest region.

What about the elective procedures? Tonsillectomies and adenoidectomies averaged 257.8 per 10,000 in the state but ranged from a low of 153.4 in one region to a high of 432.6 in another region. Thus, the difference between the lowest and highest regions was a factor of about three. The other three elective procedures, hernia repairs, varicose vein operations, and hemorrhoidectomies, while done less frequently, also showed a variation of about 300 percent from the lowest to the highest regions.

Lewis then correlated the rates for each of the operations with four variables which might explain the wide variation in rates. The four variables were: (1) the number of surgeons and general practitioners in each area, (2) the number of short-term beds available, (3) the number of board-certified surgeons, and (4) the percent of the population covered by Blue Cross in each area. There was little variation in this last factor.

The results were very informative. Appendectomy rates were highest where there was the greatest availability of hospital beds, surgeons, and doctors. In fact, 70 percent of the variation in rates between regions was accounted for by these three factors. Gallbladder operations were most frequent where the number of board-certified surgeons was higher (this is a more complex procedure that general practitioners rarely perform) and beds were more available. These two factors explained 66 percent of the variation in the incidence of this surgery from one area to another. About half the tonsillectomy and herniorrhophy (hernia repairs) variations were explained by the availability of doctors to do them and hospital beds to fill. And he found doctors tend to locate where there are hospitals.

What he found, then, was that not only do elective procedures increase when you have more doctors to do them, but so do nonelective procedures. Thus, the greater precision in the diagnosis and indication of some required surgery is called into question. It may, like elective procedures, according to Lewis be "elective only in terms of the willingness of the patient to undergo surgery, his ability to pay for the operation and the availability of resources, such as surgeons and surgical beds."

Perhaps, Lewis pointed out, some of this surgery is "ritualistic"—done because it is a customary thing to do. In concluding his report Lewis made a very telling remark: "The results presented might be interpreted as supporting a medical variation of Parkinson's Law: patient admissions for surgery expand to fill beds, operating suites and surgeons' time." This is a scholarly way of saying there is unnecessary surgery created by those doing surgery.

Three years later Doctors John Wennberg and Alan Gittelsohn studied variations in nine different surgical procedures in thirteen hospital service areas in Vermont. In order to rule out variations in surgery due to age, they age-standardized their data. They too found extensive variation in surgical procedures, especially those considered elective procedures. Of the nine operations they studied, the one most frequently performed and which showed the greatest variation was tonsillectomy. The state average was 43 per 10,000 residents, but in the two lowest areas it was 13 and 32 per 10,000 people, while in the two highest it was 85 and 151 annually. Thus, this surgical procedure was over eleven times more likely to be performed in the highest area than in the lowest area. They found there was a 19 percent probability that tonsils would be removed by age 20 in Vermont. But the probability ranged from 16 percent to 66 percent that children in five adjacent hospital service areas with similar demographic characteristics would have their tonsils removed. They reasoned that such differential rates were largely traceable to wide variations in the medical judgments of operating physicians. Doctors appear to differ widely over the indications for and the efficacy of this surgery. This may also reflect their training and their financial interests in finding surgery advisable.

They found variations in surgery for other conditions too. Differences between the high and low hospital service areas varied by a factor of 3.2 for appendectomies, by a factor of 5 for hemorrhoidectomies, by a factor of 1.7 for hernia repairs, 3.5 for prostatectomies, 3.4 for female gallbladder operations, 3.0 for hysterectomies, 4.6 for varicose vein operations, and 4.7 for dilation and curettage operations. This last minor operation was the one most frequently performed on women. While 55 out of 10,000 women had the operation in one year, the range among hospital service areas was great: from a low of 30 to a high of 141 per 10,000 females.

In their 1973 article Wennberg and Gittelsohn also pointed out some factors which explain some of the variation in rates of surgery among hospital service areas. They found a fairly high correlation ($r = .64$) between the surgery rate and the number of physicians performing surgery. They found that populations which were served by more general practitioners doing surgery tended to have higher rates for less complicated surgery but lower surgery rates for those more complex surgical procedures typically performed by fully trained surgical specialists. And those service areas served by trained surgeons tended to have higher rates for more complex surgery, while populations served by more internists tended to have lower surgery rates but higher rates of diagnostic procedures.

An interesting study to perform sometime might be to see if the amount of plumbing repairs or electrical repairs in different areas varies by the number of plumbers and electricians available. If highly trained plumbers and electricians made annual inspections of homes of people unknowledgeable about plumbing and wiring, they could probably detect quite a bit of required and elective repairs. And what about car mechanics?

In early 1970 John Bunker published in the *New England Journal of Medicine* an article that raised eyebrows and stimulated further research.

The title was "Surgical Manpower: A Comparison of Operations and Surgeons in the United States and in England and Wales." In a nutshell, he found that, by population, the United States had more than twice as many surgeons as England and Wales and that American surgeons operated exactly twice as often. For every 3,700 operations done on a population of 100,000 annually in those countries, 7,400 were done in the United States. While England and Wales had only 18 surgeons per 100,000 we had 39.

Could it be that the presence of too many surgeons leads to the situation where there is too much surgery performed? Are American surgeons under too little peer review? Do American surgeons consult too little with other specialists to determine the best treatment modality for the patient? In attempting to answer these questions, Bunker points out that consultation in Great Britain is more extensive. Two or more physicians, the surgeon, and an internist or general practitioner may get together to think through what is best for the patient. Often the internist, the nonsurgeon, sees himself "as the patient's protector against surgery." But Bunker points out that "the American surgeon, by contrast, may function as consultant exactly as his British counterpart"; however, "He may accept patients without referral, or he may be the primary physician–general practitioner, referring the patient to himself for surgery and thus creating his own demand."

A signed editorial entitled "What Puts the Surge in Surgery?" appeared in the same issue of the journal in which Bunker's article appeared. Dr. Francis Moore, commenting on Bunker's article, wrote:

Money may be at the root of it all, and among the many reasons for the excessive development of American surgery. . . . For the pecuniary-minded physician and surgeon alike, or for psychiatrist or pediatrician, the American population is a happy hunting ground. No one is held in check by any governmental system. The strictly controlled professional environment of Great Britain makes a striking contrast in surgery, as shown by Dr. Bunker; analogous data from controlled clinical environments in this country, such as the prepaid practice groups, certainly add to the conviction that the American system of payment has something to do with the frequency of operations.

But there may be another interpretation to the wide difference in American and English surgical rates. Maybe we do not have too much; maybe they have too little. Maybe we have luxury surgical care for the well-to-do while the poor go without basic medical care. In the words of Bunker, "The 'incentive' of a fee for service may tend to increase the number of operations in cases in which the indications are borderline." But, he continues, "The converse must, of course, be considered: that in the absence of such economic incentive, many procedures that are desirable but not essential may not be performed." Bunker does not rule out that there may be some surgical underutilization in the United States. But he concludes, "There is a disproportionate number of surgeons in the United States . . . and it seems likely that some unnecessary surgery is being performed."

But there were several shortcomings in Bunker's research. For one thing, the rates for surgical procedures were not standardized by age. Since the amount of surgery varies by age, and the age compositions of the two countries might be different, this could be an important factor. A second problem was that the *way* data is collected and reported on surgical procedures in the United States and Great Britain is different. This difference may help explain some of the differences in rates of surgery between the two countries. In the United States up to three surgical procedures may be counted in each hospital admission, but in Great Britain only one is included. Maybe this fact might account for the higher statistical rate of surgery in the United States. Furthermore, diagnostic procedures are not included in surgical reports in the United States but are in Great Britain.

To overcome these deficiencies, Dr. Eugene Vayda compared surgical rates in Canada with those of England and Wales, where the information is collected in nearly identical ways: surgical procedures are classified in the same way, only the primary surgical procedure for each admission is reported, data for normal obstetrical procedures are reported separately, thus allowing a comparison with nonobstetrical procedures, diagnostic procedures are included when they are the major or only reason for being admitted to a hospital, and the age and sex of each patient is recorded. Such information may be quite useful for our purposes because Canada's medical care system is much like that of the United States in terms of organization and payment.

Dr. Vayda compared the rates as between Canada, and England and Wales, for both men and women after they were age-standardized, for twenty-eight selected surgical procedures in five different categories: diagnostic procedures, elective surgery, cancer curgery, orthopedic operations, and "other" procedures. Excluding obstetrical care, the overall rate was 60 percent higher for women and 80 percent higher for men in Canada than in England and Wales. In many ways, the data confirmed what Bunker had found.

The greatest disparities were with the elective procedures, especially gallbladder removals, tonsillectomies, and hemorrhoidectomies. Men and women in Canada were, respectively, five and seven times more likely to have their gallbladders excised. And women in Canada were 3.2 times more likely to have a radical mastectomy and 2.2 times more likely to undergo a hysterectomy.

Vayda points out that there may be four major factors that could be adduced for "some of the striking differences noted in surgical rates, . . . the prevalence of disease, styles of treatment, surgical personnel and financial incentives."

With regard to the first factor, the prevalence of disease, are people in Canada, especially women who get elective procedures, that much sicker? It is unlikely, but the possibility has to be checked. When women of the same age were compared, death rates from cervical, uterine, and breast cancer were only about 10 percent lower in Canada, even though Canadian women had about 40 percent more surgery. The case for gallbladder removals is much more suspicious, argues Vayda: "For diseases of the gall bladder, the mortality rate in elderly women and men was twice as high in Canada although the cholesystectomy rate was five times higher. *Some of the excess mortality may conceivably be attributed to the increased surgery.*" (Emphasis added.) When Drs. Bunker and Wennberg saw this figure of a five times higher surgical rate with twice the mortality rate for gallbladder problems, they editorialized in the same journal issue that some surgery may "exceed therapeutic usefulness." I understand this to mean that it may cause more deaths than it saved.

The second factor, styles of treatment, may also be an important factor. For most conditions, British physicians are more likely to recommend or first try a "more conservative" approach—that is, medical treatment. Nonsurgical approaches, which typically carry less risk with them, are often used for varicose veins (injection of veins rather than stripping) and for prostatic enlargement in males. The criteria for tonsillectomy and adenoidectomy "are more fastidious and more rigidly maintained in England and Wales."

The third factor is that of who does the surgery. In England and Wales nearly all surgery is done by highly trained surgeons, whereas in Canada surgery is performed by both general practitioners and surgeons. It could be that "general practitioners in Canada perform large numbers of elective and discretionary procedures, using more liberal indications than surgical specialists."

The fourth major factor is the way surgeons are paid for their work. In England and Wales they are paid salaries. Consequently there is no financial incentive to find surgery necessary. But in Canada there is a money incentive to advocate surgery. Surgeons there are paid on a fee basis, and the more surgery they do the more money they make.

Several other facts may contribute to the differences in surgery rates. There are 30 percent fewer acute-care beds in Britain. This may limit or permanently postpone surgery, especially elective surgery, in contrast to the Canadian and American situations, where there is a surplus of hospital beds. And in Canada there are 1.4 times as many surgeons per person as in England, where their numbers are more intelligently controlled.

Now, playing detective, might we find a way to determine which of these factors contributes most to what is apparently a surplus of surgery in the United States? If we could find two groups of American surgeons, one paid salaries and the other fees for doing their work, we would have an almost perfect experiment. If we could run such an experiment, we could rule out differences in training and surgical philosophy since nearly all the doctors would be American trained. We could rule out the role of the availability of hospital beds since they are in surplus in nearly every American community. To a considerable extent we could rule out the role of national differences in the prevalence of disease. And we could even eliminate state and community variations in disease if we could find two different payment plans in the same community serving people who were about the same in a variety of demographic characteristics.

About 95 percent of the American population has its surgery done by fee surgeons, while about 5 percent has its surgery done by salaried surgeons working in HMOs (Health Maintenance Organizations). Health Maintenance Organizations number around 150 and enroll about 10 million subscribers. While there are sizable variations among HMOs, they differ significantly from fee practice. The doctors who work in them are selected by other doctors. They are paid salaries and sometimes bonuses if they can minimize costs (partly by maintaining health). They usually emphasize patient education in self-care and early disease detection in order to forestall worse cases. For a set annual patient fee nearly all services are covered, including hospitals, drugs (in some plans), diagnostic procedures, and office visits. By eliminating nearly all the financial barriers to health care, it is believed they can better maintain an individual's health. For an inclusive fee they offer a full range of physician services, including a variety of specialists.

We shall carry out our experiment to see if fee doctors do more surgery than salaried doctors. If they do, we might have strong evidence that the most critical factor in determining the amount of surgery is the fee system. However, our experiment lacks total perfection, as most experiments do. First, HMO practice usually emphasizes more peer review and consultation than does fee practice. In this regard it is more like the British system. And the opinion of one's peers is important to nearly all doctors. Second, an HMO organizes care so that relatively more emphasis is put upon disease prevention and its early detection. Whether this reduces the need for more medical care later is unknown, but it is believed it does. Third, there are usually only board-certified surgeons in HMOs, whereas in fee practice many general practitioners do surgery and some of the surgeons are not diplomates of one of the American boards. It is sometimes unofficially suspected that the lesser trained or lesser credentiated physicians may more likely engage in questionable surgery. And last, HMOs try to be more cost-conscious, at least in the eyes of their critics. This does not mean they will withhold care when it is needed. But they may not advise it when its therapeutic value is highly questionable and the cost is known. Now, let us continue with our experiment.

How does the amount of surgery and hospitalization in such plans compare to the amount of surgery and hospitalization in the free enterprise fee system? Very favorably.

One of the first studies to show this in some detail was undertaken by George S. Perrott. He compared hospitalization rates and surgical rates for federal employees enrolled in (1) Blue Cross and Blue Shield plans, (2) commercial indemnity health insurance plans, and (3) eight different Health Maintenance Organization plans (then called prepaid group plans but since renamed HMOs). The first two types use fee-for-service doctors.

The differences he found were very revealing. In 1961–62 the overall surgical rate in Blue Cross and Blue Shield was 79 percent higher: 70 surgical procedures per 1,000 for "blue" enrollees as compared to but 39 for HMO enrollees. Tonsillectomies ran 165 percent higher, "female surgery" ran 50 percent higher, and appendectomies ("emergency" surgery?) ran 85 percent higher. And total nonmaternity hospital days for HMO enrollees were 455 per 1,000 compared to 826 (81 percent higher) for Blue Shield enrollees. By reducing hospitalization the HMOs found they could substantially reduce the costs of health care.

Perrott was also interested in whether the health insurance options affected the amount of hospitalization. They did. Those with the high insurance options under the blues had 882 days of nonmaternity hospitalization per 1,000 enrollees compared to 460 for the high-option HMO subscribers. Those with the low insurance option under the blues had 520 days of hospitalization compared to 402 per 1,000 enrollees in the HMOs. In all cases, those covered by commercial insurance were closer to the blue plans but intermediate between the two.

But a word of caution must be given in interpreting these differences in hospitalization rates between the high and low insurance options. One interpretation is that where subscribers are better covered for hospitalization, physicians and surgeons will more likely prescribe surgery because they are more certain to be paid for their work. A second interpretation is that with better insurance coverage to pay the bills, a patient may decide to have surgery, especially if it is elective. And a third interpretation is that those subscribers who have had more illness in the past and/or expect it in the future elect the high insurance option because of the anticipated financial security it offers. Probably all three of these interpretations have some validity to them.

Since Perrott's study was published in 1966, a number of similar studies have been carried out. All of them, except one that was small in scope, have confirmed that there are often sizable differences in surgical rates between HMOs and fee surgeons. A Canadian comparison was made of the different hospital and surgical experiences of subscribers to two different plans. In this Sault Ste. Marie study a comparison was made between members of the District Group Health Association (an HMO) and subscribers to fee service doctors under the Prudential Insurance Company of America. Subscribers to both plans had similar age, income, sex, educational, and religious characteristics according to Hastings, the investigator. The fee-for-service patients had 26 percent more hospital separations (discharges), 36 percent more surgery, a 314 percent higher tonsillectomy rate, and 31 percent more hospital days.

In *The Medical Establishment and Social Responsibility* I compare the hospitalization rates, hospital days, and surgical rates between subscribers to a number of different Health Maintenance Organizations and either Blue Cross–Blue Shield or commercial health insurance firms in the same community. Data were available for the comparison of hospitalization rates five different times. HMOs consistently had lower hospitalization rates: 14 percent lower, 15 percent, 23 percent, 43 percent, and 53 percent lower. The number of hospital days was reduced in the HMOs from a low of 9 percent to a high of 60 percent. For example, in 1957–58 subscribers to the Kaiser Foundation Health Plan, an HMO located primarily on the West Coast, had 45 percent fewer hospital days and 52 percent less surgery than did patients enrolled in Blue Cross–Blue Shield plans.

The amount of surgery in all these comparisons was substantially lower, from 43 percent less to 58 percent less. For example, a 1966 surgical rate of 31 operations per 1,000 enrollees in the Health Insurance Plan of Greater New York compared most favorably with 73 operations per 1,000 subscribers to Blue Cross–Blue Shield in the New York area. The difference can be calculated in several ways. We can say HMO subscribers had 58 percent less surgery; or we can say patients enrolled in the blue plans had 135 percent more surgery; or we can say that for each operation on an HMO patient there were 2.35 operations on blue patients.

One problem exists in these studies which compare surgical and hospitalization rates of HMO patients to those who go to fee-for-service doctors. They do not standardize for age and sex differences. Perhaps, one could argue, there is less hospitalization and surgery in HMOs because their enrollees contain more men or more young and middle-aged people, who have less illness.

This problem has now been largely corrected in a recent study by Donald C. Riedel and five other authors in a report entitled *Federal Employees Health Benefits Program: Utilization Study.* This report is based on a rigorously designed study to follow up on George Perrott's earlier research on the differences in hospitalization of federal employees who were subscribers to either Group Health Association, Inc. (an HMO), or Blue Cross–Blue Shield health insurance benefits.

In this study Riedel and associates followed the hospital admissions for the two groups from January 1, 1967, to September 30, 1970. Controlling for age and sex differences in the two groups of subscribers as well as for differences in the benefit options in the two plans, they still found sizable differences. Blue Cross–Blue Shield enrollees had 75 percent more hospital admissions than did GHA patients. The admissions rate was particularly high for the 5 to 9, 20 to 24, and 25 to 29 age brackets among Blue Cross–Blue Shield subscribers.

This report, unfortunately, did not give data on surgical rates per se, but only on "diagnostic-specific admission rates." In only 4 of the 46 categories were GHA patients admitted more frequently—birth injuries, diseases of male genital organs, effects of chemical substances and other trauma, and wounds and burns. In 42 of the 46 categories Blue Cross and Blue Shield patients were admitted to the hospital more frequently, sometimes much more frequently. For example, they were 8 times as likely to come to the hospital for "disorders of menstruation," 5.7 times more for acute respiratory infections, 3.9 times more for tonsil and adenoid problems, 2.6 times more for breast and female genital problems, and 1.8 times more for gallbladder problems.

Two other figures are informative. When they got to the hospital, the two groups had an average length of stay which was almost identical, 6.5 days for Blue Cross–Blue Shield and 6.6 days for GHA; and the length of stay was about the same for patients in each diagnostic category in the two plans, with some exceptions. But, "There were substantial differences in patient-day rate between the two plans. Overall, for Blue Cross–Blue Shield there were 724 patient days per 1,000 membership years; for GHA it was 383." Thus, Blue Cross–Blue Shield, in comparison to GHA, was not very economical, with 89 percent more hospital days. Whether it was more medically effective is an open question. American medicine in many areas is not yet very scientific in asking the question of whether or under what conditions medical care helps. We often assume that if highly trained doctors are giving services to people they are benefiting from it. Probably in many instances they are. But in which instances are they giving services which change the outcome of an illness? This is especially questionable in elective surgery, where little research has been done in comparing the final outcome of those with and without surgery for the same malady.

The only study that does not confirm lower hospitalization and surgical rates for HMO patients than for fee patients was conducted at Washington University in St. Louis with a small sample of patients. There four doctors headed by Dr. Gerald Perkoff compared the hospitalization days and surgical rate for subscribers to the Medical Care Group, a small HMO, and users of fee doctors. While HMO patients used salaried doctors, the "control" patients went to fee physicians and surgeons for their care. While the HMO patients used slightly fewer days than did fee-paying patients, the surgical rates were nearly identical.

This finding surprised the investigators because they expected to find what had been found in other such comparisons.

Their answer to the question why there was no difference is still interesting, however. For one thing, they found both groups had low surgical rates—like those in other HMO plans. A case-by-case inspection of the 139 operations performed in each of the two groups "found no surgery which could be classified as unnecessary." Furthermore, doctors in both groups were connected with the university, although the fee surgeons often practiced in community hospitals rather than in the university hospital. And this connection to the university, although sometimes indirect, may be a factor.

University surgeons often feel that the quality of university surgery is better. They are usually the most up-to-date surgeons. On the other hand, some feel that some borderline cases of surgery may be undertaken at university hospitals in order to give training to surgical residents. In any case, several studies have shown that less unjustified surgery occurs in university hospitals, that the survival rate from cancer is higher when the disease is treated in university hospitals, and that a number of reports on the quality of care in such institutions judged it to be higher.

For example, Lembcke found that major pelvic surgery for females was justified 72 percent and 80 percent of the time in two teaching hospitals, but only 29 percent and 33 percent of the time in two non-teaching hospitals. Goss reports that 67.3 percent of the appendectomies in university hospitals were judged necessary, compared to 49.2 percent of those performed in community hospitals.

We have looked at a lot of evidence and theories in this chapter on the nature and causes of unnecessary surgery. We have noted extensive variations in appendectomies and many elective procedures such as hernia repairs, hysterectomies and other "female" surgery, gallbladder removals, tonsillectomies, and hemorrhoidectomies. Research investigators, most of them M.D.s, have suggested and found evidence that surgery is highest where there is a surplus of hospital beds, doctors, surgeons, a minimal approach to the evidence needed to justify surgery, less peer review and consultation, patients with the funds to pay for it, perhaps a higher prevalence of disease, low hospital quality, fewer trained surgeons, and the incentives of the fee system.

Following a logical experiment in which we compared rates of surgery and hospitalization under two different plans of organizing and paying for medical care, we narrowed the field of possible causes for excessive surgery. The salaried surgeon system of HMOs appears to reduce substantially the rate at which surgeons operate. But we have also pointed out that their lower rates of surgery may also be explained partially by their emphasis on health prevention, cost controls, peer review, consultation, and the selection of trained surgeons by doctors. What the relative importance of these factors is, I do not know. I suspect that the most important factors are the fee system and deficiencies in peer review under the fee system. In the next chapter we shall look at how one system of peer review, second consultations, has helped to lower the incidence of surgery within the fee system.

7

MORE EVIDENCE:
SECOND OPINIONS AND POLITICS

For many years the evidence has been growing that unnecessary surgery is frequent. In the 1950s and 1960s many accredited hospitals developed tissue committees to inspect the removal of tissue for signs of pathology. Such committees, when operated well, have reduced some surgery. But such committees have not been very successful for a number of reasons. One is that some elective procedures do not involve the removal of tissue. Another is that a lot of these committees are "paper" committees. I asked a pathologist about the situation in our own local hospital, an accredited one. He said, "Yes, I look at all tissue that is removed. But the Tissue and Utilization Review Committee does not review it." This committee does some screening of the necessity of patients being admitted whose bills are paid by Medicare and Medicaid. It also reviews their length of stay. But, he reports, "For four years they have not reviewed excised tissue for signs of pathology, let alone taken any action on it." Many such tissue committees are rather clubby affairs anyway.

But something can be done about unnecessary surgery. Dr. Eugene McCarthy and Geraldine Widmer tell what several unions did about it. Two unions in New York, the United Storeworkers Union and District Council 37 of the American Federation of State, County and Municipal Employees took action in 1972. The impetus to take action came from several sources. Many of their members were expressing concern about the quality and necessity of the care they were receiving. Furthermore, costs for hospitalization were rising rapidly.

In 1971 these two unions approached the Cornell School of Industrial and Labor Relations for help in developing a health policy. They in turn asked for help from the New York Hospital–Cornell University Medical College Department of Public Health. Out of this dialogue came two different presurgical screening programs.

The Storeworkers Union, with approximately 20,000 members, 70 percent of whom were female, developed a mandatory consultant program. If one of their members was told by a physician that hospitalization and surgery were needed, she had to get a second consultant's opinion arranged for by the presurgical screening office of the union if they wanted their hospital and physicians' bills paid. Only 16 percent of the employees hospitalized were excused from this required second opinion because they lived too far away from the consultant or could not get an appointment early enough. In contrast, District Council 37, with about 200,000 members and dependents, allowed for a second opinion but did not require it.

In both programs the presurgical screening office made appointments with appropriate surgical specialists who were board-certified. These specialists could run any tests that they liked to confirm or question the referring doctor's recommendation. The results of the second opinion were returned to the union office as well as to the referring specialists. However, it is possible that some of the union members got surgery outside the plan. But it is rather doubtful that many did.

The results of these two presurgical screening programs are enlightening. In the mandatory program of the Storeworkers Union, where people were followed for twenty-eight months, over 17 percent of the operations were not confirmed and 3 percent of the 602 originally recommended were done on an out-patient basis rather than in the hospital. The highest rate of nonconfirmation of surgery occurred in orthopedics, followed by urology, "other" operations, ophthalmology, gynecology, and general surgery.

In the voluntary program the overall nonconfirmation rate was 30.4 percent for 754 originally recommended procedures. Again, the highest rejection rate was for orthopedics (42.5 percent), followed by gynecology (40.5 percent), urology (38.6 percent), and ophthalmology (35 percent). The higher rate of nonconfirmation in this program was probably due to its voluntary nature. Women especially appeared to have "greater reservations regarding the necessity of surgery."

A third consultation was permitted if the patient requested it. But only 10 out of the 335 persons who were told they did not need an operation by the second specialist got a third opinion. If the patient desired, in confirmed cases he could get the second consultant to do the operation. Thirty percent did so. One of the weaknesses of the research design of the program, in my opinion, is allowing the second consultant to do the surgery. He too could be biased by the opportunity for new patients.

When the results of these two union studies are added together, about 24 percent of the procedures recommended were not confirmed. The costs of operating the program, mainly the consultants' fees and the office expenses, were one-eighth of what was saved. And the savings were considerable—$581,873 versus the cost of $75,268. The savings were calculated by multiplying the number of nonconfirmed cases (335) by the estimated hospital costs ($1,029), surgeon's fee ($500), and anesthesiologist fee ($125). An additional $27,783 was saved by having twenty-seven patients operated on outside of hospitals.

In addition to saving money and avoiding lost work days, avoiding surgical risk, and lessening anxiety, the program had other benefits. In some cases the consultants detected other disorders. As a result of their experience Eugene G. McCarthy and Geraldine Widmer concluded: "Because of the cost savings and the demonstrated percentage of operations not approved, presurgical screening programs appear to have a substantial benefit for any insured population."

With these results, although they were preliminary, Leo Gruskin, director of New York City's Bureau of Health Insurance, said they planned to broaden the program to include over a million municipal employees and their dependents. McCarthy said this program was the first before-the-fact program, rather than a retrospective study of questionable surgery. One case that came to light was of a woman who had trouble breathing. The first doctor told her she needed an operation to repair a deviated septum. The second doctor said she did have a slightly deviated septum but that most of her problem was due to swollen membranes. He recommended that she simply use a nasal spray. She did and this cured the problem.

But not everybody saw the report as valid. "It sounds like a very immature study to me. I don't think the judgments of the consultants were based on pre-set criteria determined by the top people in the field, so what you're getting are personal biases and differences," commented Dr. Ralph Emerson, president of the Brooklyn–Long Island chapter of the American College of Surgeons and president of the New York State

Medical Society. According to Emerson, "Based on our studies in hospitals in the Brooklyn–Long Island area, I believe there is a very low incidence of unjustified surgery." Dr. C. Rollins Hanlon, director of the American College of Surgeons, felt that such a program was mainly aimed at controlling costs by eliminating some surgery but questioned whether it improved the quality of care.

"You're caught there between free choice and a managed health system," said Dr. William Stahl, professor of surgery at New York University School of Medicine and a consultant in the presurgical screening program, as he responded to the question whether the second opinion should be voluntary or mandatory.

The patient has traditionally had the choice of what to do with his body, but unfortunately this often isn't an informed choice. Most doctors don't explain to a patient what his choices are. They say, "This is what you need, and I know everything and you know nothing." So we talk about free choice but often the patients don't have the information to make a choice.

It is interesting to note that at least one similar program had been tried earlier with great success; but it apparently had been forgotten. Sometime after World War II the United Mine Workers Medical Care Program was astounded by the excessively large number of surgical procedures being performed on its members and dependents, and the high expense of this. They suspected a lot of unnecessary operations were being performed for financial reasons, so they required that all operations had to be preapproved by a specialist. The number of operations plummeted by as much as 75 percent for hysterectomies, 60 percent for appendectomies, and 35 percent for hemorrhoidectomies.

Even before the revealing 1974 article by McCarthy was published, other unions began adopting second opinion programs for elective surgery where the need was a matter of medical judgment. New York City adopted a program for second consultations for its 110,000 municipal workers. In the first year of operation this program reduced total surgery by 28 percent and saved the city an estimated $4 million. By 1976 some twenty-eight second opinion programs were either planned or in operation.

But not all physicians see second opinion studies as valid. Dr. Sammons, an executive officer of the AMA, said that while the AMA encouraged their use, "second opinion studies are not valid measurements of surgical necessity." And for political reasons Dr. Eugene McCarthy does not talk of "unnecessary" operations but rather calls them "permanently deferred." This is because some physicians dislike differences in medical opinion being labeled "unnecessary surgery." At the same time McCarthy has not changed his mind about them: "The findings more than justify the wide adoption of second opinion programs for elective surgery for appreciable improvements in the quality of care and effective cost utilization." This was particularly true in light of the "unexplainable explosion" in surgery between 1971 and 1975 of 25 percent. And in a follow-up study of the union where 17 percent of the original physician opinions were not confirmed, only one out of eight patients had surgery in subsequent years because his symptoms persisted or worsened. This meant that elective surgery was reduced by around 11 percent.

If the scalpels of American surgeons remain as active in the future as they have been in the past, about half of America's women will undergo hysterectomies by the time they are seventy. Hysterectomies have apparently become a fad operation—they increased 25 percent between 1965 and 1973. McCarthy found that 33.3 percent of the hysterectomies in the voluntary second opinion program had not been confirmed, while 25.5 percent in the mandatory program were "permanently deferred." Mrs. Mary Barber was one woman who went without this operation in spite of what her first physician told her. She testified at the House subcommittee hearings on unnecessary surgery that her first physician told her she needed a hysterectomy because of profuse bleeding and occasional pain during menses. She took advantage of the Health Security Plan's consultation services, saw a second physician, and was offered alternatives. In this program she was one of 594 who avoided hospitalization.

In 1975 hysterectomies became the second most widely performed operation. According to figures from the National Center for Health Statistics, 725,000 hysterectomies were performed in 1975, exceeded only by 1,070,000 dilation and curettages. Together these operations constituted somewhere around 10 percent of all operations—about 17,500,000 performed in the year. They make up a sizable proportion of the $25-billion annual surgery business. In May of 1977 the House subcommittee questioned Dr. James Sammons of the AMA on the necessity of many operations. "Surgeries are being performed every day in this country that I as a physician would not agree with, ... " Sammons said to the subcommittee, but "it is a very small number."

Sammons argued it was proper to perform hysterectomies on women who have extreme fear of pregnancy or cervical cancer. A minor operation called tubal ligation makes pregnancy impossible, but Sammons said it often did not relieve "pregnaphobic" anxiety as well as a hysterectomy, a major operation. But he was disputed by Dr. Kenneth Ryan, chief of obstetrics and gynecology at Harvard and by Dr. John Morris, chief of gynecology at Yale. Both felt that hysterectomies were performed far too often. Both said that the use of hysterectomies for contraception or the prevention of future womb cancer were "excessive treatment."

Several congressmen took Sammons's reasoning to task. Representative Albert Gore said that if we followed Sammons's thinking, a person who fears cancer on his arm should have his arm amputated. Representative Henry Waxman of California asked if hysterectomies had not become a "fad operation." He also asked Sammons if he would classify as a necessary surgery mastectomy for women who fear breast cancer. Sammons replied, "If this patient has a mental problem and if a psychiatrist says it would improve a woman's mental health, that is reason for the surgery." Apparently, some doctor is always to have the last word.

Recently several researchers have begun applying the concept of cost-benefit analysis to surgical procedures, including hysterectomies. I will not attempt to show here all their reasoning and evidence, but try to summarize it. Take two hypothetical women at ages forty and fifty. What are the relative benefits and costs of going without a hysterectomy or having one in order to avoid cancer? Take the typical fifty-year-old woman with moderately severe hypertension who has not undergone menopause and has no known uterine pathology. If she has a hysterectomy, the chances are 7.5 in a thousand that she will die, thereby losing 26.4 years of expected life. If she survives, the chances are 1 in 100 that she will experience intestinal obstruction within a few years and need additional surgery to correct the condition. For a woman at this age and in her condition, the chances are about 1 in 10 that she would not survive the second operation; her life would thus be cut short by an average of 23.9 years. Overall, then, a hysterectomy for women of this age, averaged out for all women, would shorten life by 81 days.

On the other hand, the risks of not operating on this fifty-year-old woman come out to a hypothetical average loss of 22 days. There are 5 chances in 1,000 that without the operation she will die of cancer of the cervix, fundus, or ovary that, on the average, would shorten her lifespan by about 8 years. There is a 12 percent chance that she would need a hysterectomy, the mortality from which is 3 per 1,000; this death would shorten her life by an average of 24.9 years.

In this case, then, the probabilities of extending life by having the operation to avoid cancer are poor. For all such women, the average life expectancy would be decreased by 59 days. However, for all women of forty years of age, the average life expectancy would be increased somewhere around two weeks to a month.

But this is not the whole story. So far we have only looked at the relative risks of the surgery with regard to shortening or lengthening life. The total costs of the hysterectomy for a forty-year-old woman discounted at 5 percent turn out to be $5,432. Benefits other than possible avoidance of death are hard to measure. Are the improved sense of well being, fewer cramps, and the feeling of avoiding some cancer worth the risks and financial costs of the operation, the possibility of postoperative complications, the recovery from the operation? From the viewpoint of society with its heavy investment in borderline surgery, it probably is not worth it, but it may be for the woman.

One of the reasons the House subcommittee on unnecessary procedures undertook its investigation was the extensive cost of funding operations paid for from Medicaid and Medicare funds. The regional and national variations in the incidence of surgery funded by federal programs raised many eyebrows and called for second opinions to control what appeared to be surgical abuses.

In 1975 the Department of Health, Education and Welfare collected data from about 30 states on the incidence of surgery among Medicaid recipients. The average of the 26 states reporting with complete data was 18,716 operations per 100,000 Medicaid patients compared to 7,940 operations per 100,000 for the entire country. Poor people, this reveals, were operated on 2.36 times more frequently than the national average. Almost 2 million operations were performed on just over 10 million people on Medicaid in 1974. Nobody knows how reliable these figures are, however. Since sickness, unemployment, and poverty due to hospital costs are related, it could be that this figure is not very accurate. Perhaps being out of work and being in the hospital forced some people to go on welfare and thereby swelled Medicaid recipients in an unrepresentative way.

But a comparison of the different states' incidence of surgery under Medicaid was simply astounding. North Carolina had 44,887 operations per 100,000 Medicaid enrollees in contrast to Arkansas's 3,973 operations per 100,000. Is there over eleven times as much disease among North Carolina Medicaid recipients as among those in Arkansas?

And the rates on particular surgical procedures were unbelievable. Only 78 per 100,000 Medicaid children in Mississippi had their tonsils out. But in Nevada 1,709 out of 100,000 Medicaid children had their tonsils taken out, nearly twenty-two times as many. Gallbladder removals among Medicaid enrollees were 42 per 100,000 in Alabama but 579 in Louisiana, over thirteen times as high as in Alabama.

Is it any wonder that at the House subcommittee hearings on unnecessary surgery many individuals testified on the need for second consultations before surgery? Dr. Eugene McCarthy testified that he would "strongly endorse the idea that second opinion programs be a part of Medicare and Medicaid."

Government information on Medicaid hysterectomies was perhaps the most revealing. In the twenty-two states that provided adequate information on this operation, it was found that 20,016 hysterectomies had been performed on an eligible population of 6,609,684, for an extrapolated national rate of 303 per 100,000. Nevada had a rate 73 times as high as Mississippi and over 24 times as high as Ohio. In Nevada the rate was 2,488 per 100,000 compared to 34 for Mississippi and 101 in Ohio. Can the need for this type of operation vary so much from state to state?

In light of the effect of second opinion consults in reducing surgery, a number of programs are being started to cut swelling hospital and medical care costs and to save people from unnecessary surgery. But second opinion studies and plans are not going unquestioned by some leaders of the medical establishment.

At a meeting of the New York Trial Lawyers Association in the spring of 1977, officials of the organization proposed that New York State pass legislation requiring that a hospital's chief of surgery or a special surgical board certify that each elective operation is necessary. Daniel H. Mahoney, president of the group, said, "Since the peer group in the medical profession has failed to quell or even cause this to slow down to a trickle, it's obvious that legislation is necessary."

But a trustee of the Kings County Medical Society and the New York State Society of Internal Medicine, Dr. Norman S. Blackman, called the lawyers' proposal "one of the most ridiculous proposals I have ever heard." He said, "Medical judgment is not a matter of voting. If two doctors say no and one says yes, this is no guarantee that this operation is not needed."

The trial lawyers convention chairman said "knife-happy" surgeons were behind unnecessary surgery, while President Mahoney said the reason was "money." Calling unnecessary surgery an "assault" on a person and "a definite category of medical malpractice," the lawyers argued that the time to review surgical cases was "before surgery rather than after complications or death, as is now the case."

In order to control burgeoning Medicare and Medicaid costs, in 1974 the Department of Health, Education and Welfare said that each state, in order to continue receiving federal funds for certain hospital-based health care services, must have a utilization review program. Under the original proposal each patient had to be certified by a utilization review committee as needing hospitalization before he arrived at the hospital.

Under pressure from doctors, hospitals, and the AMA, these regulations were modified. The new regulations, published in November of 1974 and to go into effect on February 1, 1975, demanded only that a necessity for hospitalization be reviewed immediately after the patient got to the hospital and that nonphysicians participate in making the determination of the necessity of hospitalization.

But before these regulations could go into effect, the AMA filed suit in a Chicago federal district court which effectively blocked their implementation. The suit was settled in September of 1975 with the understanding that new regulations would take into account AMA objections to the earlier ones. The AMA had contended that only those admissions traceable to physicians with a demonstrated history of poor utilization needed to be reviewed. Of course, this would have nearly eliminated the regulations since hospital peer review is often weak if it exists at all.

The next HEW regulations said that utilization review had to be completed within three days of admission. Critics argued that such regulations would be gutless—performed, perhaps, after the patient had already had unnecessary surgery. To get around this possible objection, the HEWs new regulations now said that utilization review had to be performed before any elective surgery was done. But the regulations do permit exceptions to this when the patient is in pain. Patients were also to be reviewed periodically about the appropriateness of their length of stay. These new regulations went into effect on June 1, 1975.

However, many hospitals have balked at the rules because they say they don't have the money to hire the people to conduct such reviews. In New York City about 60 percent of the hospitals were balking at the drive to implement the utilization review program and were being threatened to have their federal funds cut off. They felt the new guidelines would hurt their hospitals by reducing the number of patients coming in for surgery. But Donald Rubin, president of the Consumer Commission on the Accreditation of Health Services, felt that the new regulations should be implemented. "The new utilization review regulations can save billions of dollars by preventing inappropriate hospitalization and unnecessary surgery." He argued that consumers and the government should not capitulate again to the AMA, which had "dictated government health policy" for too long.

In January, 1977, U.S. District Court Judge George C. Pratt ordered New York State to resume reimbursement for surgery deemed nonurgent. The suit was brought against the state by the 28,000-member state medical society, two physicians, and a female patient. The patient was reported to be in need of a dilation and curettage for "voluminous and frequent menstrual bleeding." However, she could not pay for her operation, and under a state Medicaid ruling that went into effect in May of 1976 the state was denying reimbursement for all operations that could be deferred "without jeopardizing life or essential functions or causing severe pain."

In arguing for payment for the operation, the state medical society argued that the State Social Services Law was unconstitutional because it would result in unequal treatment between Medicaid and paying patients. But in his thirty-page opinion Judge Pratt said he was basing his ruling on the conflict of the state law with the federal Social Security Act. Under that act, he said, "if an eligible person seeks an operation which is medically indicated and ordinarily performed on other persons in comparable medical circumstances, then that person is entitled to Medicaid coverage." While this patient may have been medically needy, the principle of "ordinarily performed" meant that deferrable operations no longer would be deferred. The jduge's ruling was expected to result in $5 million additional expenditures annually for hospitalization and surgical services for nonurgent surgery.

Despite some objections to second opinion programs, they are being adopted in a number of states for Medicaid and Medicare patients, for union members, by Blue Cross and Blue Shield, and by commercial insurance firms. Massachusetts, for example, began utilization review for Medicare and Medicaid hospital admissions in 1975. This decision followed a statement by Massachusetts Welfare Commissioner Jerald L. Stevens that hospitals and other providers of medical care were guilty of bilking the Medicaid program with the provision of unnecessary surgery and other needless procedures. However, utilization review has rarely lived up to its expectations of substantially reducing medical care expenditures. Beginning in March of 1977, Massachusetts Medicaid recipients had to get a second opinion if they were told they needed elective surgery for one of eight different conditions. The eight conditions were those most often judged to be unnecessary: tonsillectomy and adenoidectomy, cholecystectomy, hysterectomy, hemorrhoidectomy, disk surgery and spinal fusion, cartilage and joint surgery, repair of nasal defects, and varicose vein removal. In the fiscal year 1976 5,200 such operations were performed on Medicaid patients at a total cost of about $5.6 million. According to Richard Knox, "State welfare officials believe that when this program is applied to the Medicaid population on a mandatory basis, it will save $1.3 million the first year in deferred surgical costs and 27,500 days in the hospital." After the costs of second opinions, additional diagnostic tests, and administration are subtracted, he says, "the state expects to achieve a first-year net savings of $500,000."

Already this crackdown on questionable surgery is beginning to pay off in Massachusetts. After only three months in operation nearly half of the tonsillectomy and adenoidectomy cases were denied, as were 20 percent of the hysterectomies and 12 percent of certain nasal procedures. At the bottom of the list, however, only 3 percent of the disk surgery and spinal fusion operations were denied.

A number of firms in Massachusetts, as in other states, have worked out arrangements with Blue Shield to have a second opinion program. Some health insurance executives are unsure whether second opinion programs will reduce the number of operations, stifle inflationary hospital costs, eliminate the risks present in marginal surgery, and generally improve health care quality. Dr. James Sidel, who has been working with Raytheon's second opinion program for its 25,000 workers, says many questions are unanswered even though second opinions contraindicate about one-third of elective surgery. "This does not mean that the surgery is 'unnecessary,'" Sidel emphasized. "There is frequently an honest difference on a permanent basis—or at least up to two years." Furthermore, one of the advantages of this program, according to Sidel, is that "if surgery is indicated, the patient will feel much more relaxed about the need for it." Thus, a second opinion which confirms the first physician's advice for it may help patients feel it is really needed.

At the House subcommittee hearings on unnecessary surgery, "the consensus of the witnesses, regardless of their attitude on unnecessary surgery, was that anyone who has been told that surgery is needed should get a second opinion from another physician," according to Francis Cerra. However, Cerra believes, the probability of getting surgery under prepaid plans which use salaried surgeons is much less. In 1973 the probability of a United States woman getting a hysterectomy by age seventy was 45.3 percent, but only 16.8 percent in a prepaid (HMO) plan. While nationally 30.1 percent of all children have a tonsillectomy, only 10.5 percent do in prepaid plans. And nationally 17.5 percent of all men eventually get a prostate operation, but only 7.7 percent get one if enrolled in a prepaid group. But since over 95 percent of the United States population gets its health care from fee doctors who find surgery more advisable, second opinions have been adopted in some areas.

In mid-1976 New York State, for example, passed a law which allowed a second opinion on surgery, for which Blue Cross and other plans pay. Some of these plans are being designed on an experimental basis to see if surgery is reduced and costs controlled. And a majority of the members of the American College of Surgeons, 75 percent in fact, endorse obtaining second opinions. But in responding to Blue Cross's selected use of second opinions, the AMA president Dr. Max Parrott said, "Blue Cross is just trying to hold costs down and is not thinking of the patient. What makes the second guy's opinion more valid than the first? The consultant sees the patient only once and doesn't know the problem nearly as well as the first doctor, who is familiar with the patient's history."

One factor which may make the second physician's judgment more valid is whether he is allowed to do the surgery. For example, in one New York plan—Teamsters Local 25—the second surgeon may not perform the operation. Furthermore, many plans require that only a board-certified surgeon be allowed to give the second opinion. The joint study by the American College of Surgeons and the American Surgical Association found that tonsillectomies were performed in most instances by noncertified surgeons or nonsurgical specialists.

A number of commercial insurers have begun offering the second opinion program to group customers on an experimental basis. For example, Aetna Life and Casualty began a one-year voluntary test program for its own 10,000 Hartford area employees and their dependents on November 1, 1976. By July of 1977 only five persons had obtained a second opinion. According to Gerhard R. Schade, who helped design the Aetna pilot program, "It is too early to tell whether the program will reduce surgery or cut costs." But he pointed out that many employers are interested in the program.

He also pointed out that the program could have several other beneficial fallouts. "It encourages claimants to investigate the necessity of surgery with their own doctors" even if they don't get a second opinion, because of the publicity that surrounds such programs. He also pointed out that if the second surgeon confirms the first doctor's recommendation, this may reduce malpractice cases; however, if he doesn't, and this only happens in a minority of cases, it could lead to more of them.

I asked him how they felt about the consultant doing the surgery. He said, "We operate on the principle that the patient has the right to choose his doctor." But, he went on to explain, "we think it unfortunate if the second doctor undertakes the surgery. If he does, then we don't pay the second doctor a consultant's fee because then it is a preoperative consultation." He believed it would undermine the medical profession's support of the program if many consultants ended up doing the surgery.

Aetna's experience so far is that few claimants are using the voluntary program of consultants. But for those few who do use it, it could make patients more thoughtful and secure about undergoing surgery. And it could make physicians more careful in their diagnostic judgments and recommendations if they knew their patients could get a second opinion.

But the most recent evidence indicates second opinion programs can significantly reduce questionable surgery. On March 1, 1978, Blue Cross and Blue Shield of Greater New York released the preliminary results from its two year long plan of offering second opinions to wary patients. Of 1,500 cases in which subscribers obtained consultation from a second physician, the first doctor's opinion about the need for surgery was not upheld in one quarter of the cases. The highest rate of nonconfirmation was 33.2 percent found among 253 orthopedic cases. Dr. A. Eugene Silberry, executive vice president of the Blue Cross–Blue Shield plan estimated that in two years of operation the second opinion program had saved $700,000. However, he noted that many patients were not getting a free second opinion and that unconfirmed patients would have to be followed for many years to see how many of them had operations "permanently deferred." Still, the prospects are bright for second opinion programs to significantly reduce the amount of surgery in the United States.

8

THE QUALITY OF AMERICAN SURGERY

"Unnecessary and meddlesome operative intervention go hand in hand with poor surgical care, and they are surely a part of the surgical scene in the United States." This statement, by Dr. Francis Moore, points to another but not separate aspect of the quality of American surgery.

So far we have looked at the quantity of American surgery. Available evidence suggests it is in oversupply. While unnecessary surgery could be well done in a technical sense, the fact that it is done at all suggests that some surgery is of poor quality. But what about the surgery that is deemed necessary?

There is more to surgery than cutting and sewing. Dr. William Nolen says, "What goes on in the operating room is important, even critical, to a patient's survival and well being. But faulty preoperative preparation or careless management can ruin even the finest of surgical procedures and spell disaster for the patient."

To Dr. Calvin B. Ernst surgery is more than what goes on in the operating room. It involves "preoperative care, intraoperative judgment and management and postoperative care." This Lexington, Kentucky, surgeon continues, "To paraphrase Frederick A. Collier, 'I can teach a janitor to operate, but not practice surgery.'" To this surgeon surgery involves "total" care.

Most nurses are in a better position to judge the quality of medical care in our hospitals than are laymen. In early 1977 *Nursing* magazine polled its members about the quality of care that was provided in the hospitals, institutions, and nursing homes where they work. Over ten thousand readers responded to the seventy-eight item questionnaire and, in addition, over two hundred sent letters about their complaints and observations. While the response cannot be interpreted as representative, a majority felt that United States health care deserved no better than a low B grade. Fully 38 percent of the nurses said they would not want to be treated at their own hospital if they had a choice. Prompted by this, I asked a nurse about the hospital in the community where she lived. Her response: "I'd never go there if I didn't have to."

The medical skills of their doctor colleagues were generally highly regarded by the nurses; 28 percent considered them excellent, 53 percent good, 19 percent below good. However, over three-quarters of the nurses assessed doctors' psychological support of sick patients as either fair or poor.

Perhaps one of the most eye-opening figures involved known fatal accidents: 42 percent of the nurse respondents said they were aware of deaths that could be attributed to physicians' mistakes. And 15 percent of the nurses reported they had witnessed such mistakes more than once. One nurse said that a general surgeon in her hospital had lost eight patients in an eight-year period by "sheer ineptness."

Apparently many of the letters were like one that Ann Landers received from a laboratory technician about the debate concerning doctors burying their mistakes and protecting their colleagues. The person who signed herself "Penna Tech" reported she had worked in a small hospital for eleven years. "The doctors are mainly interested in the welfare of the patients. However, I can tell you that a fair number of 'mistakes' have been buried in this place. . . . Surgeons have cut arteries, perforated intestines and screwed up in assorted ways. The erring surgeons were never censured. . . . What is worse is that the families of patients never knew the truth. 'Complications' can cover just about any mistake." Then "Penna Tech" reported that one doctor who had been an alcoholic for fifteen years "did a lot of damage" when he was "boozed up." She reported a doctor who, though senile, was still practicing at eighty. "He had a loyal following of devotees who adored him, but I wouldn't let him treat my dog."

Just as there are variations in the incidence of surgery from place to place, there are also variations in the quality of surgical care in the United States. These variations are apparently due to a variety of factors such as the training of surgeons, how they are paid, the amount of surgery they do, the quality of the facilities where they work, as well as their own medical skills and personal qualities.

On a simplistic basis, we might think of surgery ranging along a continuum. At one end of the continuum are highly trained physicians working with an excellent team of assistants in a magnificently equipped hospital. At the other end are general practitioners not trained in surgery, whose diagnostic skills are poor and who work in hospitals not adequately equipped for the work they are doing. But the actual situation may be considerably muddier than this. There are highly trained physicians who do poor work just as there are physicians who are inadequately trained for surgery yet do a good job. Some surgeons may do too much surgery for their own good or that of their patients, while the surplus of surgeons that exists may not allow some to keep their skills honed by constant practice.

Good surgical care involves a lot more than deftness in cutting and sewing. It involves good judgment in diagnosis, quick and accurate decision making in the operating room—especially if problems arise—and good management of the patient after surgery. And not least, the doctor needs to be humane in his concern. This is so because the patient undergoing surgery is often in an emotional crisis. He is confined to a strange place without the established routine of work and daily contacts with family and friends. He is often in pain over which he feels he has little control. He may be faced with the money problems that the high cost of hospital surgery entails. And while the doctor may have reassured him that 95 percent or 99.3 percent of the patients undergoing this operation survive, he still knows that he will be 100 percent dead if he is in that 5 percent or .7 percent mortality group.

It is easy for a surgeon undertaking his thousandth operation to forget it is the patient's first or second, with all the apprehension it brings. "We get caught up in the science of medicine. We worry about selecting the proper pills, choosing the best operation, ordering the appropriate x-rays; and we neglect the art of medicine," comments William Nolen, a surgeon. "We forget that we are not dealing solely with an abstract scientific problem, but rather are treating a human being—one who is, in all probability, extremely apprenhensive, frightened of what he or she may have to face. Too often we doctors do our jobs as scientists but fail as humanists."

Dr. Nolen says that in preparing a patient for surgery he tries to follow a two-word rule: "No surprises." While it may be a surgeon's hundredth gallbladder removal, it is not for the patient. Nolen describes his own procedure:

Before the patient goes into the hospital, I sit down with her and explain exactly what is going to happen. I tell her about the sleeping pill she'll get in the evening, the shaving that will be necessary, the enema she'll have to have. I tell her about the injection she'll get preoperatively that will make her drowsy and her mouth dry; about the needle that will be put into her vein in the operating room; about what it will be like to wake up in the recovery room. I warn her about the discomfort she'll have postoperatively and about the painkillers that will be available to alleviate her distress. I try to anticipate everything that will be done to her and for her so that she won't be frightened by the unexpected. Mental preparation for an operation is at least as important as physical preparation.

Nolen admits that "occasionally I slip up." And so do other doctors. Nolen tells about how disconcerting it was to him when the physician who was treating him for coronary artery disease made a serious error. He reports he was as upset emotionally as any other patient about the presence of angina (heart pain) and the possibility of a life shortened by either coronary artery disease or the surgery from which one out of twenty to fifty patients do not survive. Survival of course depends on their preoperative general health, their age and, the skill of the surgeon.

The sequence of events as described by Nolen in *Surgeon under the Knife* went like this. Noticing some heart pain after fairly strenuous exercise, Nolen made an appointment to have a "stress electrocardiogram" done on June 18, 1975. This test involves taking a base electrocardiogram before any exercise is done. Then the patient begins running on a treadmill with the electrocardiographic lead wires still attached to appropriate places on his body. Unless problems show up early in the electrocardiographic tracings, the pitch of the treadmill is increased so that the patient has to run harder. As these tracings are followed, they will indicate if the heart is getting enough oxygen to meet the demands of stress. In Nolen's case, abnormalities showed up in the tracings, and he again experienced the burning sensation in his chest as a result of the exertion. The physician who ran the stress test advised him that he needed a second diagnostic test, an angiogram, to detect which coronary arteries were giving him problems. The first physician recommended that he see a Dr. George Smith (a fictitious name).

His physician sent the abnormal electrocardiograms to Dr. George Smith, and Nolen made an appointment to see him on June 24, six days after he had had his stress test. During those six days Nolen was emotionally depressed because the stress EKG had revealed he had heart problems. He had to explain to his six children and his wife about the serious nature of his problem and how it could lead to a heart attack. But he arrived on time to see Dr. Smith on June 24. The three-day schedule was to involve a general physical exam the first day, an angiogram on the second day with observation overnight to make sure there were no complications from it, and release by noon the third day.

On the first day Dr. Smith explained to him that he had just looked at the results of his stress EKG even though he had had them for six days. Dr. Smith told him, "I don't like the looks of the EKG. It's impossible to say with certainty—I could be wrong—but most of the time when we see a pattern like the one here it means three-vessel disease." (Three-vessel disease is more serious than one- or two-artery vessel disease, is much less likely to respond to medical treatment than to surgical treatment, and shows an 83 percent chance of five-year survival after surgery, compared to a 92 percent chance with one or two vessel disease.) Then Smith continued with a statement that shocked Nolen: "If that is the case, then we generally like to proceed with surgery soon after the angiogram. We might wait to the next day, but sometimes we take the patient directly from the angiogram room to the operating room. I think before we proceed with the angio we'd better have a surgeon in to see you so he'll be on call in the morning. Whom would you like me to call?"

Nolen had thought he was coming for a diagnostic test only, and here was the doctor telling him he might need surgery the next day. He had given no thought yet to surgery, let alone who he wanted to do it if it was needed. Nolen said he felt "as if I'd just been unexpectedly handed a notice informing me that I was tentatively scheduled for execution in the morning."

After collecting his senses, he said he wanted to think about it. He talked it over with his wife and the referring physician, who expressed dismay that Dr. Smith had not looked at the EKGs until that day even though the referring doctor had reminded him twice about it. Nolen felt strongly that Dr. Smith should have looked at the EKGs earlier and should have forewarned him that surgery might be immediately advisable. Nolen then called a series of physician friends, some of whom advised him to go to a hospital where they did heart operations every day.

To make a long story short, Dr. Nolen did not have the angiogram or the heart surgery done at this hospital. About two weeks later he had it done at Massachusetts General Hospital. The operation was a success. But the point of this story is that in Nolen's estimate Dr. Smith had made a grave error in the management of his case. Nolen writes:

There isn't a physician alive who hasn't, at least once, been guilty of an error in judgment. Any honest physician will admit that he can remember cases in which one or more of the decisions he made proved in retro spect to be wrong, and as a result of his misjudgment the patient suffered. But honest errors in judgment—mistakes—are one thing; they hurt, but a reasonable patient will forgive them. Errors in management that occur because a doctor neglects to do his job are another matter. I feel no obligation to forgive the doctor guilty of that sort of practice.

After commenting that Smith "hadn't been guilty of malpractice in any legal way," he felt he "nevertheless was guilty of malpractice." Showing the usual mutual protectiveness of physicians about their mistakes and errors in management, Nolen concludes, "As a physician, I'm reluctant to criticize Dr. Smith, but as a patient, I shall let the criticism stand." In reflecting on this matter with his wife, Nolen wondered whether, if he had not been a physician, he would have simply picked a surgeon as Dr. Smith suggested rather than withdrawing from his poorly managed case. His wife said, "I think you would have.... It's so hard to question a doctor."

This story about Dr. Nolen's problem as a patient of Dr. Smith only points to one area where surgical care is sometimes faulty in American medicine. No rigorous studies are available to show how well patients are humanly managed by surgeons.

But there is evidence that some surgical care in the United States is faulty. Recently a House subcommittee heard evidence that 78 percent of the "preventable" deaths or complications that occurred in hospitals resulted from surgery. These findings came from a "Critical Incident Study of Surgical Deaths and Complications" sponsored by the American College of Surgeons. Ninety-five hospitals from seven states participated in the study which analyzed 1,696 "life-threatening complications." When a death or troublesome incident occurred, a judgment on its preventability was made immediately by the surgical staff of each participating hospital. While the study presented to the subcommittee did not go into great detail, the findings were revealing. Of the 245 patients who died after surgery, 85 could have been saved. And almost half the life-threatening incidents among surgical patients could have been avoided.

In 1976 the *New York Times* published a five-part series of articles about incompetent surgeons and questionable practices by many doctors.

One of the articles was headlined "U.S. Doctors: About 5 Percent Are Unfit." This article agreed with a number of other studies that about 16,000 of the nation's 320,000 physicians are mentally ill, addicted to drugs, or ignorant of current medical knowledge and practices. These incompetent physicians were estimated to treat 7.5 million patients annually and "may account for tens of thousands of needless injuries and deaths each year." This writer argued that such doctors should either have their license revoked or undergo further training and practice under close supervision.

While the American surgical profession is probably the best trained in the world, there are some doctors who are faulty in their surgery. Take the case of a woman who was experiencing severe abdominal pain. After being diagnosed as needing her gallbladder removed, she entered a New York municipal hospital, where the operation was performed. During the operation the surgeon noticed a tumor on her kidney. Without taking a biopsy of it and having it checked by a pathologist for malignancy, he removed the whole kidney during the gallbladder operation. The woman died shortly after surgery. The medical examiner's report showed why. The surgeon had removed the woman's only remaining kidney! He didn't know she had only one because no x-ray had ever been taken. Moreover, the removal of the kidney had been unnecessary because the laboratory report showed the tumor on it to be benign.

Another New York patient, a middle-aged man, entered a city hospital to have replaced a heart valve damaged by rheumatic fever. Upon being taken off the heart lung machine following the operation, he died in minutes. The autopsy revealed that the surgeon had put the artificial heart valve in backwards, preventing blood from being pumped through the heart.

To illustrate the problem of some poor surgical care, including unnecessary surgery, the *New York Times* made an estimate of the number of operations performed in the United States in 1975, the deaths that occurred following surgery, the percent not recommended (based upon a *New York Times* estimate using the opinions of a number of doctors), and the number of avoidable deaths. For example, there were 724,000 tonsillectomies, 70 percent of which were not recommended, 150 deaths from them, of which 105 were avoidable. There were an estimated 223,000 prostatectomies, 2,700 deaths from them, and 783 avoidable deaths, with 29 percent of the surgery not recommended. Of some 472,000 gallbladder removals 6,700 resulted in death, of which 938 were avoidable because surgery was not recommended in 14 percent of the cases. Or of 787,000 hysterectomies, 374 of the 1,700 deaths could have been avoided if surgery had not been undertaken where it was not recommended.

According to estimates of the National Center for Health Statistics, about 18 million operations were performed in 1975. Over 250,000 of the patients died during or soon after surgery. Now, it must be said that many of these patients would have died without the surgery because they were critically ill, even though over three-quarters of all surgery is considered "elective." Furthermore, many others had their lives extended or painful conditions relieved. But about 1 out of 72 dies following all surgery, and about 1 out of 200 dies following elective surgery, even though mortality rates differ significantly from one procedure to another. While some of these deaths are due to the risks of surgery and anesthesia, some, but an unknown number, are due to bungled surgery which may not have been needed in the first place.

One patient out of 5,000 to 10,000 who are operated on will die from anesthesia. Being put to sleep by a general anesthesia is always risky because the powerful drug interferes with the functions of the respiratory system, the heart and blood vessels, the brain, and the kidneys. And a few patients have an anesthesia reaction which leaves them brain damaged. Authoritative estimates say about 3,000 people die annually from anesthesia administered during surgery.

A report on 41 patients who filed or whose relatives filed a malpractice suit was recently culled from the files of a malpractice insurance firm This report found that 8 of the patients suffered brain damage and that 30 died from anesthesia. The chief cause of the problems was that insufficient oxygen was given during anesthesia, but nine cases involved gross mismanagement.

In California in 1967 a forty-five-year-old man died following plastic surgery on his ear because the oxygen tank ran out of gas. No one noticed it until the man's brain and heart were already irreparably damaged. Some hospitals now use a beeper warning system to indicate when the tanks are running low. Despite the known hazards of taking anesthesia, only about half the cases are managed by fully trained anesthesiologist M.D.s.

Another study involved the inspection of ninety-six mishaps or near-mishaps in the administration of anesthesia at the Massachusetts General Hospital. Interviews with twenty-seven anesthesia specialists revealed that half the patients were adversely affected either mentally or physically.

Of the ninety-six mishaps 27 percent were attributed to equipment failure, while over two-thirds were charged to "human error."

Surgeons and other physicians may cause as many as thirty thousand deaths annually from improper prescriptions. According to Boyce Rensberger, "Perhaps ten times as many patients suffer life-threatening and sometimes permanent side effects, such as kidney failure, mental depression, internal bleeding and loss of hearing or vision."

How good are doctors in their prescribing practices? Take antibiotics, for example, a class of drugs supposedly overprescribed. From 1967 to 1971 the use of these drugs grew six times faster than did the population. In 1974 4,513 doctors took a fifty-item multiple choice test on antibiotics. Only 50 percent got a score of 69 or better. Those who scored lowest were those who had been in practice longest or who saw the most patients in their office daily. Only 11 percent of those who had been in practice over fifteen years scored 80 percent correct or above on the test, compared to 26.7 percent of those in practice five years or less. Sometimes a doctor accedes to patient demand for the drugs or gives them because they make him appear to be "doing something" for the patient.

But on the other hand, what they are doing can sometimes be harmful rather than helpful. According to Dr. Herschel Jick of the Boston University Medical Center, an estimated 300,000 people are hospitalized annually in the United States because of drug reactions. This makes it one of the ten leading causes of hospitalization. Dr. Jick estimates that one adverse drug reaction occurs in eighteen hospital drug prescriptions, with about 10 percent of the reactions considered major and over 1 percent fatal. Another hazard from the case of antibiotics is "superinfection." In the use of antibiotics to combat an infection, a worse infection by a microorganism resistant to antibiotics may develop. Once super-infections start, they are frequently difficult to stop and are often fatal. As many as five thousand people may die annually from antibiotic reactions, 20 percent of which prescriptions were not needed in the first place.

United States doctors prescribe twice as often as do Scottish doctors, but we may not be healthier for it. To be knowledgeable about the twelve hundred drugs available is no easy task. Many doctors over-rely for their information on the drug salesmen or the glossy medical journal advertisements of the pharmaceutical houses. They do not keep up with the scientific literature on drugs.

A side note is of interest here. After the *New York Times* published its five-part series on unnecessary surgery, incompetent doctors, poor prescribing habits, and drug deaths and complications, pharmaceutical houses retaliated. They canceled advertising valued at $500,000 from *Modern Medicine*, a subsidiary of the *New York Times* but run wholly independent of it. In spite of the fact that *Modern Medicine* ran an advertisement in the *New York Times* dissociating itself from the newspaper and the five-part series, stating it was not consulted on the series, two hundred pages of advertising valued at $2,500 per page were canceled. An officer of *Modern Medicine* said that the advertisers who canceled their ads felt that "you don't feed people who beat you up."

An important factor in the quality of surgery is the training of those who do it. It is a sad fact of American medicine that any doctor, whether trained in surgery or not, can perform surgery. And some general practitioners want to do it because they can earn more that way. This is not to say all general practitioners doing surgery are poor at it or that all board-certified surgeons are good. But some evidence exists that the surgical care offered by doctors who have had three to six years training in it is better than that of those with a few months exposure to it. It stands to reason.

In 1957-58 less than half of all surgical in-hospital procedures performed in the United States were done by certified surgeons. Today about 30 percent of all American doctors do some surgery. This means that of 94,000 physicians engaged in surgery only about 52,000 are fully trained and board-certified. We will show evidence in chapter 9 that even many of the board surgeons are not busy enough to do the five to ten operations a week that are needed to keep their skills sharp. Yet some physicians poorly trained for surgery are undertaking major surgery but only doing it a few times a year.

Dr. Alex Gerber is one doctor who feels that only doctors fully trained in surgery should be allowed to do it. But he points out that some general practitioners try to maintain their operating privileges even though poorly qualified. He asserts, "There is practically nothing that some general practitioners consider themselves unqualified to do, including formidable operations that would tax the skills of the most eminent surgeons in the country." While some develop "a modest proficiency in the technical aspects of surgery," he contends, "more often they flounder around the abdomen like a fish out of water." He feels that they lack the judgment in many cases to make correct diagnoses. He says, "I have known GPs to remove a woman's uterus to cure headaches and constipation.

Worse, I have known of a case where biopsy examination showed the patient to have a malignancy in the lower part of the uterus and where the doctor removed only the upper part, leaving the cancer behind."

He further documents his case by citing the use of the outmoded uterine suspension. He says, "You could examine the operating room schedules of good hospitals for years without finding one listed. Yet I have known GPs to do this operation on teenagers as young as fourteen to cure irregular menses." He contends that "in some 'Mickey Mouse' hospitals, such operations are scheduled quite frequently." He tells of another GP who, on his first attempt to do a gallbladder operation, used a GP assistant who had never done one either. "The result was disastrous," according to Gerber.

How do general practitioners get operating privileges? Dr. Gerber contends that "ordinarily reputable surgeons operate at reputable hospitals, nonsurgeons [meaning doctors untrained as surgeons but doing surgery] at disreputable places." But sometimes there are exceptions made. "It is not uncommon for hospitals that have raised their standards and now scrutinize closely the credentials of all new doctors to have a few old practitioners who have had operating privileges for many years and who, for sympathetic reasons, are allowed to retain them." Gerber contends that "some hospitals are just plain lax about whom they will give surgical privileges to and about what those doctors then do." He argues that this tends to be true in proprietary hospitals run for a profit and some small nonprofit community hospitals. He tells of one group of California GPs, who were denied operating privileges at other hospitals, simply opening up their own and deciding who could do what. And he tells of another California hospital where "trained surgeons tried to keep out of the operating room men whom they deemed unqualified. The effort boomeranged. The untrained men gained control of the hospital governing board, threw the trained men off the key committees, and set up their own peer review body."

Some general practitioners keep surgeons out by running a closed hospital—closed to surgeons. In *A Surgeon's World* Dr. William Nolen tells how he felt that because "in most big cities there are too many surgeons" he would go to a small town or city to start practice after he finished residency training in surgery. He wanted to keep busy. One town he visited was in Massachusetts. It had a population of twenty thousand and not a single surgeon. He made an appointment with the chief of staff of the hospital. Nolen told him he would like to practice surgery there. The man, a GP, said a lot of other surgeons would too and then went on to explain why Nolen would not get hospital privileges there. He said:

In simple terms—we don't want a general surgeon here. You see, Dr. Nolen, this is a GP community with a GP hospital. Every member of the staff is a GP, and we like it that way. We all do some surgery; what we can't handle we send to Boston. Now, if we let you in here, what's going to happen? Very shortly there will be other specialists. And soon after that they'll be running things and they'll squeeze us GPs out. The obstetricians will tell us we can't deliver babies, the internists will tell us we can't read electrocardiograms, and you'll tell us we can't take out any appendices. We'll be left with nothing to do but treat kids with runny noses and women with backaches. It's happened in other hospitals and it will eventually happen here; but we're going to fight hard to keep it from happening for a while yet.

GPs and other inadequately trained surgeons are doing a lot of surgery in this country today. They are sometimes accused of being the ones who do more unnecessary procedures and botch more operations than others. In the words of Dr. Nolen, "We doctors have built a medical system that works wonderfully in some spheres; poorly in others. The fee-for-service system, by its very nature, may lure the unwary physician into behavior that is economically motivated, less than admirable, even unscrupulous." Even if a doctor orders tests that are objectively known to be unnecessary, he can claim he is doing it for the good of his patient. And the system is slow to correct such abuses. As Nolen puts it:

The system stifles self-criticism. The surgeon who accuses an internist of prescribing unnecessary medications will receive no more referrals from the internist; the orthopedist who tells a general practitioner that he has mismanaged a fracture will never see another of that GP's patients. Silence, even in the face of wrongdoing, is the only safe policy. If you want a thriving practice, keep your mouth shut. The medical profession does not tolerate traitors.

What can be done about the poor and unnecessary surgery that occurs in the United States? In addition to what individuals can do such as getting second opinions and seeking out trustworthy and skilled doctors, a number of steps could be taken by three institutional bodies. These bodies are medical societies, state licensing boards, and hospitals.

One group of bodies that can deal with questionable surgical practice is the local and state medical societies and their parent organization, the American Medical Association. However, since these are voluntary organizations which contain only about half of all United States physicians, they have been notably lax in disciplining physicians. Furthermore, while the laxity is somewhat understandable it is lamentable. "There is a great reluctance on the part of doctors to interfere with another doctor's reputation and means of livelihood," comments Dr. Robert Derbyshire, an authority on the disciplining of physicians. "The philosophy apparently is that a man's reputation is more important than the welfare of his patients."

I collected statistics on what disciplinary procedures were undertaken by all state medical societies over the nine-year period from 1960 to 1964 and 1966 to 1969. While there are estimated to be about 16,000 physicians who may not be very good, in that nine-year period only 72 members were expelled by state medical societies. They constituted only 7 percent of those disciplined by the state medical societies in some way. But the disparity of state medical society disciplining activities was rather astounding. During the nine-year period seven states had not undertaken a single disciplinary action against an errant physician, while Massachusetts undertook 159 and Texas 128. In fact, eight state medical societies with only 16 percent of the nation's physicians accounted for 60 percent of the state medical society disciplinary procedures!

The bodies with the most power and the legal authority to revoke licenses and discipline physicians are the state medical boards. In addition to licensing and registering doctors, they may take such actions as restricting their practices, putting them on probation, and taking away their licenses or their right to prescribe medicine. How effective have they been in detecting and disciplining an apparently sizable number of physicians who are alcoholics, drug users, unethical in their practices, and incompetent? Again, from the statistics I culled on state medical board disciplinary activity I would have to conclude that many of them are not very effective. Over the nine-year period cited earlier, the state medical boards undertook only 4,398 disciplinary procedures, of which 654 involved revoking licenses. Collectively the boards revoked only 2.7 licenses annually for every 10,000 physicians. If an estimated 16,000 United States physicians are poor, in any one year only about 70 or 80 of them will have their licenses revoked. Dr. Robert Derbyshire reports about the same pattern of annual license revocations from 1971 to 1974: 89, 77, 37, and 88 respectively for those four years.

Both I and Dr. Derbyshire have found that some states are active in medical discipline while others appear to be doing very little. For example, in the 1960–64 and 1966–69 periods the state of Hawaii undertook no disciplinary procedures, while Oregon undertook 520 at a rate of 212 per 10,000 physicians. In comparison to Pennsylvania, Oregon was eighty-five times more likely to take disciplinary action and fourteen times more likely to revoke a license. If we compare the eight states with the highest revocation rates to the eight states with the lowest license revocation rates per 10,000 physicians, the differences are rather unbelievable. The high states were thirty times more likely to revoke a physician's license than the eight states with the lowest rate of revocation. Could it be that some states attract a lot more bad apples than others? Or is it that some states simply are more vigorous in their medical disciplinary activities?

Dr. Derbyshire, who has been critical of the policing functions of many state societies, believes they need to become stronger to weed out bad doctors. He tells of a doctor who performed gallbladder operations on three different patients and in each of them tied off the wrong duct so that the patients died. It took weeks of investigation and days of hearings before this man lost his license.

In light of the growing number of malpractice suits and the estimates of poor and incompetent doctors, what are the states doing about it? Take New York state's multi-staged and complicated system of detecting poor medical care. If a patient or somebody else has a complaint about a doctor, he presents it to the state's Professional Medical Conduct Board, which has jurisdiction over about 55,000 doctors. Then one of twelve overburdened investigators, each carrying a load of about forty-five cases, checks it out. If he feels the complaint has some justification, it goes next to a screening committee. If they believe the case has merit, it then goes to the attorney general's office, which prosecutes the case before a committee of the Medical Conduct Board. That body passes on its verdict to the commissioner for review. He then makes a recommendation to the State Education Department, responsible for licensing functions. Then the case continues to climb to the Regents Review Committee, the Regents Committee on Professional Discipline, and ultimately the Board of Regents, which makes the final decision. The commissioner of education implements any action called for. These nine steps may be why the agency had a backlog of 551 cases in late 1976. The New York Consumer Protection Board's task force on medical discipline concluded the medical discipline system "bends over backward to provide professionals with an unprecedented degree of due process which would not be tolerated if extended to criminal defendants or business regulatees."

But these nine steps are not necessarily the end. If the doctor wants to appeal his case, he can: first to the appellate division of the state courts and then to the court of appeals. In Richard Peck's estimate, "By this time, conceivably, some other patient has been hurt, or the doctor himself has been hit with a nasty malpractice suit."

Apparently very few doctors and medical societies report on the misconduct of fellow physicians, for fear of reprisal. Richard Peck reports that in one year the New York City medical society received nearly 900 complaints but passed on only 13 to the state's Professional Medical Conduct Board. According to the AMA's fourth principle of medical ethics: "The medical profession should safeguard the public and itself against physicians deficient in moral character and professional competence. . . . They should expose, without hesitation, illegal or unethical conduct of fellow members of the profession." However, until some states passed legislation giving immunity to doctors who report on negligent practices, most doctors have been extremely hesitant in exposing fellow physicians. To do so would not only expose them to the threat of reprisal and libel suits but would dent the secrecy and camaraderie of the self-protective medical profession. Only three states have passed legislation requiring doctors to report on incompetent doctors, but twenty-six states grant immunity to them if they do. One state that has passed both pieces of legislation is Arizona. When its law went into effect, the reporting of unfit doctors quadrupled.

State medical boards could do more than simplify their procedures and beef up their staffs to investigate complaints about poor doctors. They could require so many hours of continuing education periodically for doctors to retain their licenses. Or they could require physicians to be relicensed or recertified periodically by passing examinations. Many feel that this is the direction efforts must take to improve the quality of medical and surgical care. They argue that improving health care involves not only ridding the profession of a few flagrant violators but upgrading the training of many physicians to keep them up to date.

"We are standing on the threshold of convulsive recertification moves," Dr. John Gramlick told members attending the Southwestern Surgical Congress in 1976. As president of this society he feels "time is running out on the independent and uncoordinated efforts that have long been the hallmark of hospital and health care continuing education."

New Mexico was one of the first states requiring continuing medical education for physicians to retain their licenses. In 1971 the legislature passed a bill that allowed the state licensing board to establish requirements for relicensure. In 1972 the licensing board said a physician must complete 120 hours of continuing medical education every three years to stay in practice in that state. By 1975 28 of 1400 physicians there had not met that requirement. They either retired or moved out of the state. Today twelve states have similar mandatory requirements. But the system will not be as effective as it could be until all states have such requirements. Outdated physicians who do not want to get involved in such programs can simply move to a state where they are not required.

Specialty boards are also investigating recertifying processes to maintain and upgrade physician skills and knowledge. But they are moving slowly. Eleven of the twenty-two specialty boards have indicated they will require some kind of recertification in the future. The American Board of Internal Medicine gave its first recertification examination in 1974; of the 14,000 internists who took the exam, 150 failed. The American Board of Surgery will put a recertification program into operation by 1985, but the mechanism by which this will be done has not yet been formulated. According to Dr. Gramlick, however, "All certificates issued to diplomates of the American Board of Surgery from 1975 forward will be for ten years only."

The third group of bodies that could investigate physician conduct are hospital staffs. They are closer to the problem of unnecessary and incompetent surgery and medical services than are the more distant state licensing boards. But they too are sometimes plagued by the close association of physicians who rarely want to threaten the livelihood of fellow practitioners.

Hospitals are particularly important for surgeons, for they are the location of most surgical work. The evidence is that the quality of surgery varies greatly among some hospitals. In fact, the variation is so great that the staff of the Stanford Center for Health Care Research concluded that "the degree of variation in quality is large enough to constitute an important public health problem. . . ."

The staff of the Stanford Center for Health Care Research recently completed a thorough and sophisticated piece of research on the *outcomes* of surgery. Outcomes, they argued, are the "ultimate validators of the effectiveness and quality of medical care." Their study had two parts to it. In the "extensive" part of the study, they looked at the mortality rates of 314,000 patients in 1,224 hospitals who had surgery in one of fourteen surgical categories. Controlling for variations in the mix of patients at various hospitals, they found that death rates at some hospitals for the same disease and surgery were over two times as high as at other hospitals.

In the more detailed "intensive" part of the study, 8,593 patients who underwent one of fifteen operations at seventeen participating hospitals across the country were thoroughly evaluated before and after the surgery. Extensive data were collected on each patient's socioeconomic characteristics and the nature and extent of his disease so that the likely outcome from surgery could be compared to the actual result. Information was also obtained from the anesthesiologist, the surgeon, the nurses, and about the hospital where the surgery was performed. Two negative outcomes, mortality and morbidity (complications), were then evaluated after surgery was performed, the cases being chosen in such a way that similar patients were compared. In this way differences in the outcomes of surgery could be attributed to the surgeons or the hospital by eliminating the fact that some hospitals might get a mix of sicker patients than another hospital.

Patients were evaluated both one week and forty days after surgery and the actual outcome compared to the expected outcome in light of each patient's condition. After appropriate statistical adjustments were made, six of the seventeen hospitals had more deaths or complications than were expected. The worst hospital had two and one-half times more deaths or severe morbidity than the best hospital. At the best hospital 45 percent fewer patients either died or had severe complication than were expected, while at the worst hospital death or severe complications were 40 percent higher than expected. Severe complications or death, overall, was highest for lower limb amputations (27.9 percent of the patients) and craniotomies (26 percent) and lowest for vaginal (0 percent) and abdominal hysterectomies (1.3 percent).

The researchers were also surprised by some of the other findings of the study. Contrary to what they had expected, the outcomes from surgery appeared unrelated to the size of the hospital, to whether it was a teaching institution, or to whether it had a higher percentage of board-certified specialists. But they did find that surgical outcomes were better where there was a higher proportion of registered nurses on the staff, and where care was taken in awarding staff privileges to doctors.

People often assume one hospital is as good as another. But little research has been done on the hundreds of unaccredited hospitals where it is often easier for a physician to get staff privileges. Some of these hospitals are owned and operated by physicians for a profit. Even going to a hospital accredited by the Joint Commission on the Accreditation of Hospitals does not always mean the hospital is living up to set standards. The federal government did a random survey of 261 accredited hospitals between January, 1974, and October, 1975. Its findings: 64 percent of the hospitals failed to meet one or more of the accreditation standards.

Nevertheless some hospitals are making progress in controlling unnecessary and poor surgery. But it is rarely due to their own voluntary efforts. It is due to the fact that since 1974 the Joint Commission on the Accreditation of Hospitals (JCAH) has been pushing a "quality assurance program." And the major part of this program consists of a medical auditing system that is used to monitor the quality of surgical outcomes and identify careless or uninformed doctors or those doing excessive numbers of operations where the justification for them is nonexistent or suspiciously borderline.

Many hospitals feel they need the accreditation stamp of the JCAH if they want to attract top-notch doctors, to receive increasingly questioning patients, and to have their financial claims to medical care honored by many insurance companies. Of the nation's 7,200 hospitals about 5,000 are accredited. However, only about 60 percent of them are carrying out proper audits to evaluate medical care. But those involved in developing audits say that their systematic use can help reduce the hazards of surgery stemming from long-standing problems of poor surgical performance and unjustified surgery.

Many instances can be found where medical audits and subsequent remedial efforts have produced positive results. For example, a year-long audit of all hysterectomies performed at one Virginia hospital revealed that in 31 percent of the cases normal uteri were removed. The hospital's department of obstetrics and gynecology then proceeded to develop more precise criteria for diagnosing the need for this operation. Another audit a year later found that the removal of normal uteri dropped to 16.5 percent.

Another hospital found that its auditing revealed an unusually high number of complications following Caesarean sections performed there. The reasons were that general surgeons were doing them without the presence of an obstetrician-gynecologist better trained in recognizing and treating maternal and neonatal problems. The hospital then decided that only obstetrician-gynecologists could perform this operation.

A Wisconsin hospital audit of appendectomies revealed one "operator" who was removing an usually high percentage of normal appendices. The evaluation diplomatically suggested that the doctor was "improperly diagnosing" appendicitis. He was then ordered to attend an appropriate education program. More important, he was told to have a consulting surgeon examine his appendectomy patients before surgery.

Corrective procedures were instituted at a midwestern university hospital where a "high" 5 percent of the patients were suffering from thrombophlebitis after surgery because intravenous needles were being left in too long. And by auditing another hospital detected that its high incidence of urinary tract infections following surgery were traceable to the improper use of catheters.

Effective physician surveillance can simultaneously improve the quality of surgery and reduce unjustified surgery. This conclusion stems from a study carried out by the College of Physicians and Surgeons of Saskatchewan beginning in 1972 and reported on in 1977. Saskatchewan Department of Health discovered that the number of hysterectomies being performed was rising at an alarming rate. Between 1964 and 1971 hysterectomies in the province increased over 72 percent even though the number of women over fifteen years in the province had increased less than 8 percent in the same time period. It also found wide disparities in the proportion of women getting hysterectomies in the three largest cities in the province. The committee doing the study established criteria for justifying surgery and then all province physicians were informed of them. Before the criteria were announced, a sample of seven hospitals revealed 23.7 percent of the hysterectomies performed in them unjustified by the criteria; but after the criteria were in effect for several years the percentage of unjustified hysterectomies declined to 7.8 percent. Furthermore, the total number of hysterectomies dropped nearly 33 percent between 1970 and 1974 indicating that the work of the committee and attendant publicity about unnecessary hysterectomies had "made doctors more critical in their judgment of when a hysterectomy is required."

Without such auditing, which many hospitals still lack, many surgical shortcomings in hospitals were not known to exist. If they existed, they often could not be easily traced to careless nurses, sloppy doctors, institutional malfunctioning, or patients' noncompliance with therapy. But, according to Charles M. Jacobs, a former director of the JCAH quality review center, medical auditing for the first time enables a doctor's performance over time to be assessed. It is a better way to assure continuing competency while board certification assures competency only at the time of examination—maybe twenty or forty years ago.

While auditing can help correct surgical abuses, it is done poorly in some hospitals and not at all in others. One pathologist I spoke to about surgical auditing said that it was practiced more widely in the 1950s than it is now. While he said it can be an important teaching device for physicians—a way to catch errors and poor diagnosis—it was "embarrassing for surgeons to have their work reviewed by others." As a pathologist he felt he was in the unpopular role of a "henchman"—reporting on the deficiencies of a doctor.

Medical auditing or peer review will not work or work effectively to correct surgical abuses if it does not receive the support of doctors. And many doctors who do surgery do not want to be regulated by anybody. They want to judge their own competencies, and sometimes they do in ways that are beneficial to themselves.

Peer review by cronies in the same hospital may sometimes work, but the evidence is that it is invoked in only the most flagrant cases and even then not consistently. Dr. William Nolen, for one, believes:

Doctors just cannot be relied upon to police themselves. We're too afraid of hurting the feelings of our confreres, of losing referrals from them, of being overcritical. We lean over backward in order not to judge our fellow doctors too harshly, and often we do this to such an extreme that it poses a threat to the well-being of patients. A surgeon practically has to become a mass murderer before his fellow surgeons will take away his surgical privileges.

While some contend that only physicians can judge the competence of doctors, Nolen disagrees. "It's a myth, perpetuated by the medical profession, that 'only doctors can judge other doctors.' Intelligent laymen, with technical help from doctors, could do it better." He concludes, "In fact, lay participation is an absolute necessity if we're ever going to have really effective cost and quality control in medicine."

In an article entitled "See No Evil," one doctor tells of his small midwestern hospital's response to a critical internal audit. Doctor X, writing in the March, 1976, *Quality Review Bulletin,* which keeps names of doctors and hospitals confidential, reports that members of his hospital's medical staff executive committee became concerned with the "unusually high" number of patients admitted for tonsillectomies and adenoidectomies. He states, "One physician scheduled seventeen children for T & A on one day." An audit committee was set up and proceeded to "establish specific criteria to evaluate admissions for T & A and to justify the surgery." But, he reports, the physicians in the audit "appeared nonchalant about the need to document their reasons for subjecting children to surgery. . . . Only 10 percent of the 50 cases scrutinized met the justification criterion." He also believed that the fact that 50 percent of the operations were being performed on children under five years of age "indicated indiscriminate use of adenotonsillectomy." He writes:

The audit committee could only conclude that performance weighed against established criteria, was poor. Indications for surgery were not documented; critical management was not properly instituted when complications were identified; histories and physicals were not completed properly nor were they entered on the chart at the appropriate time; progress notes did not reflect clinical activity; and postdischarge planning was absent.

What happened to the audit committee's report? After it was sent to a number of other committees, the chief of staff, and the chairman of the department of surgery, it was discarded and a new audit committee established by the chairman of the department of surgery. Even the falsification of medical records by one physician was not acted upon. Doctor X concluded:

If we are to do more than pay lip service to quality, then physicians must accept criticism and peer review to assure this quality or anticipate that outside governing agencies will do that for us.

9

TOO MANY SURGEONS?

There is evidence of considerable excess surgical capacity and substantial unnecessary surgery; both support the conclusion that a misallocation of doctors exists. [Erwin Blackstone]

We're going to have so many general surgeons trained that the only way they could make a living would be to cut everything human that looks like a bump. [Walter Bornmeier, M.D., former AMA president]

Approximately 43.5 percent of cholecystectomies paid for by Blue Shield in Mississippi in 1972 were performed by non-board-certified surgeons. Small hospitals have difficulty in enforcing credentials when beds are empty and the budget is overextended. [James D. Hardy, M.D.]

The heart of the problem lies in too many people performing surgery. Fully one-third of the total surgical manpower pool is made up of non-certified surgeons and general practitioner surgeons. [George D. Zuidema, M.D.]

Many people believe that an excessive number of doctors doing surgery has one major cause and two major effects. The major cause is that the high fees and income of surgeons has attracted too many doctors into it, while we have a deficiency of primary care physicians. The major effects are that we have too much surgery being performed as a consequence, and that some surgery, needed or not, is poorly done because it is done by physicians not fully trained to do it or who do not operate often enough to keep their skills sharp.

Until recently little thought has been given to the need and supply of different kinds of doctors. A number of manpower studies in the

1950s and 1960s looked at the number of physicians available—and usually found a shortage of them. Most of these studies, however, did not look at the relative distribution of doctors among the specialties. They apparently assumed, rather naively, one of two things. They assumed that either a doctor is a doctor or that doctors would somehow automatically go into the specialties in the right numbers to meet the medical needs of people. But all doctors are not the same, and a disproportionate number were attracted into surgery, especially general surgery, where the general surgeon was seen as "king of the mountain." But as William Nolen observed a while back, "general surgeons, on the other hand, in the big cities and their suburbs particularly, are a dime a dozen."

The first of two questions I want to investigate is, how many surgeons are there. But the answer to that question is different from the answer to how many doctors are doing surgery. And that is the problem. There are a number of physicians doing surgery who are not trained for it. And with the loose credentialing system we have for physicians in the United States, any GP can perform any surgery he wants to if he can find a place to do it. Dr. Alex Gerber says there is "one small hospital in southern California that I know of where a single unqualified surgeon performed more of one particular type of kidney operation in ten years than all the surgeons at the Mayo Clinic together have done in fifty."

"Incredible as it may seem, *millions* of operations are performed each year by physicians who have had no special surgical training," reports Dr. Gerber. And it could be that surgically untrained men are more likely to find surgery necessary in equivocal situations. And it may also stand to reason that surgeons who are working to only 50 percent or 70 percent of capacity, as most are, may find surgery necessary where diagnosis is uncertain. Dr. James Hardy writes: "There can be no doubt that some unnecessary surgery is performed, but it is hard to quantitate." He also says, "That the institution of straight salaries for all surgeons would diminish the number of operations performed is possibly true," although he admits uncertainty about how it would affect the quality of care. "In another context," he continues, "an internist of the writer's acquaintance claims that he can get any patient operated upon: it is simply a matter of choosing the right surgeon."

We might classify physicians who do surgery into three classes, in descending order of their qualifications to do surgery.

Class 1 surgeons would be doctors who have received training in surgery and passed the examination of the appropriate specialty board which certifies them as competent in general surgery or in some specialized field such as ophthalmology, urology, or obstetrics and gynecology. Class 1 surgeons are "board-certified" surgeons.

Class 2 surgeons are those who have undertaken special training in surgery, usually a residency program, but either did not take or took and failed some specialty board examination for surgery. These surgeons are sometimes said to be "board eligible" surgeons. Both Class 1 and Class 2 are "surgical specialists" by training. Interns and residents in surgical training programs can be placed in this category.

Of particular concern here is the makeup of those entering surgical training programs. Large numbers of medical students trained in foreign medical schools are entering these programs. Yet their medical training in some foreign programs is often inadequate and "the majority exhibit a serious deficit in English language communication," according to Dr. James Hardy. They make up 30 to 50 percent of surgical residency programs, but usually not the better ones. According to Dr. Hardy, "They often populate marginal residency training programs, with limited clinical material, and their knowledge and understanding of human physiology is often thin." Since many do not return to their country of origin, their presence here, he says, represents "at times a less totally effective surgeon than would a native born American who had graduated from a United States medical school."

Very large numbers of foreign medical graduates go on to practice surgery in the United States even though they do not have the skills to become board-certified surgeons. From 1970 through 1974 51 percent of the foreign medical graduates failed the written exam and 40 percent the oral exam of the American Board of Surgery, in comparison to 14 percent and 15 percent respectively of fully American-trained physicians. If the foreign trained surgeons were reexamined for certification, 71 percent failed the written part of the examination, and 50 percent the oral part. Nevertheless, many went on to practice surgery.

Class 3 surgeons are those who claim a specialty in surgery but did not undergo any special training for it. And because they did not have any special training they are not eligible for board certification. Usually they are general practitioners, and some medical specialists, who do some surgery and received their M.D. degree prior to 1968.

In 1976 there were approximately 52,000 board-certified (class 1) surgeons, whose numbers were expected to increase to about 57,000 by 1978. The estimated numbers in particular surgical fields in 1976 were: general surgery, 14,103; obstetrics-gynecology, 11,195; ophthalmology, 6,630; orthopedic surgery, 6,417; otolaryngology, 4,341; plastic surgery, 979; urology, 3,690; thoracic surgery, 2,186; neurosurgery, 1,566; and colon-rectal surgery, 334.

But in addition to approximately 52,000 board-certified surgeons in 1974 there were 12,000 surgical residents in training, 20,000 non-board-certified surgical specialists, 9,000 GPs, and 1,500 osteopaths who performed surgery. Thus, about 94,000 United States doctors, over 30 percent of all active doctors, were doing surgery. This is a higher percent than for any other nation in the world.

Now, suppose we want to find out how much surgery each of these three classes of physicians is doing. One way to do that is simply to look at what percentage of all operations each class of surgeons performs. We will do that in a minute. But one limitation to this approach is that it does not take into consideration the complexity of operations, which ranges from the quick and simple to the very long and complex. To get at the relative time needed for and the complexity of an operation, an index has been developed by physicians to weigh numerically different surgical procedures. This index is called the "California Relative Value" (CRV) of an operation. By the use of this index each procedure is given a "weight" based on the time taken to perform it, the postoperative care, and the complexity. For example, an abdominal hysterectomy is given a weight of 16, for it is a fairly complex procedure that requires substantial time to perform and requires considerable postoperative care. In contrast, a tonsillectomy, a simple procedure requiring little postoperative care, is given a weight of 4. Thus, four tonsillectomies are considered equivalent to one abdominal hysterectomy. Some other CRV weights may be helpfully illustrative: 1, local excision of a skin lesion; 4, a dilation and curettage, or a vaginal delivery; 5, breast biopsy by excision; 14.5, cholecystectomy; 30, excision of cartilage located between vertebrae; 40, repair of abdominal aortic aneurysm; and 52, heart valve replacement. A typical or average operation is weighted at "9." CRV weights are a rough index to the surgical fee—that is, the higher the weight, the higher the surgeon's fee, as a general rule.

Now, the understanding of this index is important to getting a grasp on what classes of surgeons do what types of surgery. Counting the number of operations doctors perform is a rather crude index for computing how much surgery they are doing. This is because doing one heart valve replacement (52 CRV) is considered about the equivalent of doing five appendectomies (9.5 CRV) or thirteen normal deliveries (4 CRV). An average or typical operation with a weight of 9 is illustrated by a hernia repair.

We do not have nationwide figures on the numbers and CRV weights of operations performed by all doctors. However, various researchers have gathered extensive data on the number of surgeons, the number of operations they perform annually, and their operative workload in four areas of the United States which are highly suggestive. Each of the four areas designated in table 1 contains about a million residents, with at least one city of fifty thousand or more, a medical school, and defined hospital service areas. This table shows that class 1 surgeons do around 52 percent of the operations whose CRV percentage rates go from 55.3 percent of the operations to 59.6. Class 2 surgeons, non-board-certified specialists, do anywhere from 15.3 to 30.3 percent of the operations with a range of CRV weights from 13 to 28.3 percent. Interns and residents do from 4.8 to 20 percent of the operations with a similar variation in CRV-weighted surgery. General practitioners and other doctors do anywhere from about 8.7 to 24.9 percent of the operations with CRV weights from 7 to 14 percent.

Now, what does all this mean? After reclassifying surgical residents, if we extended these area studies to the whole country we could say: (1) that board-certified surgeons make up 31 percent of the doctors doing surgery, that they do 58 percent of the principal operations and do 65 percent of the CRV-weighted operative work; (2) that non-board-certified specialists make up 17 percent of the doctors doing surgery, do 24 percent of the principal operations, and do 23 percent of the CRV-weighted operative work; (3) that general practitioners, excluding a few other doctors who do a little surgery, make up 27 percent of the surgical manpower, do 13.5 percent of the principal operations, which account for only 9 percent of the CRV-weighted operative work. Most of the general practitioners do fairly simple surgical tasks—they do 26 percent of the deliveries, 23 percent of the tonsillectomies and adenoidectomies, about 17 percent of the diagnostic dilation and curettages, and 12 percent of the inguinal-hernia repairs. While these figures cannot be reliably generalized to the whole country, they do suggest that general practitioners are still doing a substantial amount of surgery. The researchers who conducted this research *"conclude[d] that far too many physicians perform surgical operations and that work loads of surgical specialists are modest."* (Emphasis added.)

TABLE 1

Percentage Distribution of Operations and CRV-Weighted Operations in Four Areas*

	Area A		Area C	
	All operations	CRV-weighted	All operations	CRV-weighted
Board-certified specialists	53.0	58.1	49.7	55.3
Non-board-certified specialists	30.3	28.3	24.3	25.4
Interns or residents	7.0	6.6	4.8	5.2
GPs or other	9.7	7.0	21.2	14.1
	Area B		Area D	
	All operations	CRV-weighted	All operations	CRV-weighted
Board-certified specialists	50.6	57.3	53.4	59.6
Non-board-certified specialists	15.3	13.0	17.8	17.1
Interns or residents	20.0	21.3	9.9	10.5
GPs or other	14.1	8.4	18.9	12.8

Areas A and C are in the Northeast, B in the Southeast, and D in the Northwest.

*Adapted from the American College of Surgeons and the American Surgical Association, *Surgery in the United States,* 1975.

What do they mean by modest work loads? While there are variations by specialty, the board-certified specialists averaged 199 "typical" operations (a typical operation is weighted at 9 by the CRV index) a year, the non-board-certified only 132. Some surgical authorities believe surgeons need to do about 250 operations a year to keep their surgical talents honed. About 10 percent of the board-certified surgeons are performing 350 or more operations a year now. Most would be capable of doing 300 or more operations a year, and would like to, but with the number of doctors doing surgery there simply is not enough work to go around. The surgeons averaged forty-six hours of work a week, and then some of this time was spent in primary care activities.

A team of researchers headed by Rita Nickerson asked, "What if only board-certified surgeons did all the surgery in the U.S.? Could they handle it?" The answer is yes. If they did, each would be doing about three hundred typical operations a year—comparable to the numbers performed by surgeons in England, Sweden, and in prepaid group plans in the United States.

They suggest that we probably would have better surgical care and perhaps less unnecessary surgery if either we limited surgery to (1) surgical specialists (classes 1 and 2) or (2) board-certified surgical specialists (class 1 surgeons). "It is clear," they argue, "that there is no need to have surgical operations performed by both nonsurgeons and well-trained surgeons." Furthermore, they point out that a few board-certified specialists, some class 2 surgeons, and many class 3 surgeons do so few operations "as to raise questions about the maintenance of skills." They found, for example, that about 30 percent of the physicians doing surgery were doing only about five a year. They suggest that a better trained but "smaller corps of surgeons could maintain the present volume of surgical operations."

One other advantage would result if surgery was restricted to the better-trained surgeons. Some young surgeons have their skills atrophy from disuse as they struggle to establish a practice over a period of years. With fewer physicians doing surgery, much of this problem would be rectified.

Now, the reader may ask, "Then why not cut back on the people who are allowed to do surgery?" In answering that question we enter the area of medical politics. Older GPs and non-board-certified specialists often believe they are as good surgeons as the board-certified ones. In some cases they are probably right. Furthermore, who is going to make such decisions? Politicians do not want to tackle it. Specialty boards can suggest that it be done, but as voluntary associations with only quasi-legal powers, they lack the authority to put such a suggestion into effect. Furthermore, if they did so, they would be accused of protecting their financial interests. And it is beyond the power of medical societies to do even if they were so inclined. That leaves us with hospital boards and hospital staffs who can determine the credentials of the doctors who practice there. But because of cronyism among practicing surgeons who want to protect the livelihood of some fellow surgeons at some hospitals, the changes will have to come slowly to eliminate nonsurgeons from surgery. Meanwhile some patients will suffer from less than optimal surgical care from untrained doctors who do so few surgical procedures that their skills do not remain sharp, or from trained practitioners who are not busy enough either.

Other studies support the claim that we have too many surgeons who are not busy. Dr. Edward Hughes studied how nineteen general surgeons used their time in a New York suburban community. He found that this group of surgeons averaged a 34-hour work week of which only about 9 were spent in the operating room. Nearly 6 hours a week were spent on personal activities and meals on the job, leaving about 29 hours "devoted to professional activities" each week. These surgeons were found to be averaging 3.1 "hernia equivalent operations" per week; a full work load is postulated to be about 10 per week. In testifying to a House sub-committee, Dr. Hughes said that the average workload of these surgeons was 43 percent less than a postulated full workload and that the median workload was only one-third of it. (This means that while a few surgeons in this community were quite busy, the majority were not.) He said this suggests an inefficient use of costly and highly specialized medical skills; and it may contribute to operating in equivocal situations with resulting higher costs to consumers and the government.

How do the findings in this small study compare to a prepaid group practice where the surgeons were salaried? Quite poorly. Dr. Hughes also studied a health maintenance organization with 158,000 enrollees who employed seven board-certified surgeons full time. These doctors did 9.9 hernia-equivalent operations per week, which was seen as a full load, and did over three times as many operations as were performed by a group of fee surgeons in a community practice he had studied earlier. In contrast to 9.8 surgeons per 100,000 population in the United States as a whole, this group of surgeons met the surgical needs of its patients with only 4.4 surgeons per 100,000 population. Dr. Hughes felt this group of surgeons was able to keep the quality of surgical care high by constantly doing the kind of work they were trained for. Dr. Hughes concluded that the prepaid group achieved economy in the utilization of services by doing outpatient surgery when possible, by limiting hospitalization to what was necessary, and by keeping all its surgeons busy.

In summarizing informed opinion we must conclude: (1) that there are too many physicians doing surgery; (2) that this results in pressures to do unnecessary surgery and that some of the surgery is being carried out by men poorly trained for it or by men not sufficiently busy to maintain their surgical skill and judgment at optimal levels; (3) that we have too many surgical residency training positions that will contribute to an even larger surplus of surgeons in the future; and (4) that some of these positions are being filled by foreign medical graduates whose medical knowledge and skills are open to question.

What can be done to correct this situation? Hospitals could become more selective in whom they allow to do surgery. Of the 5,770 short-term nonfederal hospitals, over 26 percent (1,534) remain unaccredited by the Joint Commission on Accreditation of Hospitals. (Osteopathic authorities accredit 128 along similar standards). While all hospitals must be state licensed, this means little. The federal government or even state governments could require that all hospitals be accredited if they want to receive Medicare or Medicaid funds. But even accreditation does not ensure that hospitals will be careful how they give surgical privileges or whether they will operate appropriate audits to minimize unnecessary and poor surgical care.

With 50,000 operations performed daily in the United States, about 6,000 of them will continue to be performed by general practitioners not always trained for it, until local hospital authorities act. Perhaps only pressure by consumers and state and federal bodies interested in the quality of health care can force hospitals to restrict surgical privileges to those who deserve them. When 438 of 701 members of the Society of University Surgeons responded to the question of who should be doing surgery, over 94 percent agreed that "all surgery (except minor procedures) should be performed by surgeons who are either eligible for certification (within three to five years of completion of approved training) or certified by their respective surgical specialty board." The SOSSUS report concluded, "The problem of an excessive number of persons doing surgical operations appears to be soluble only through stricter hospital regulations for the granting of surgical privileges."

Surgical training programs also need to be cut back. Unless they are drastically cut, we will have more surgeons per population in the future than we already have. Approximately 16,000 surgical residency positions exist in the United States. About 2,500 to 3,000 new surgeons a year complete these three to five year training programs when only about half this number are needed.

In addition, some would argue for a curtailment of foreign medical graduates entering surgery since they constitute nearly a third of those entering surgical training programs. Some of this might be accomplished by eliminating the many marginal training programs as surgical residency positions are cut back.

Other steps can also be taken to reduce the number of surgeons and poor surgeons doing surgery. One is periodic reassessment of the fitness, performance, and competence of surgeons by their recertification by specialty boards, who would require continuing education and reexamination for permission to do surgery. Some have argued that surgery by GPs could be reduced if they were paid a lower rate for surgery than surgical specialists are by Medicare and Medicaid and by health insurance carriers.

10

SURGICAL FEES, FEE SPLITTING, AND GHOST SURGERY

"Medical and surgical fees are a matter of tradition, not logic," asserts Dr. William Nolen. Physicians' fees are usually high enough to put physicians in the top 5 percent of income statistics wherever they live. And perhaps the standard of living of the locality in which they live, be it Sandusky, Ohio, or New York City, partly determines what they charge. Some believe the going rate can be translated into "what the traffic will bear."

In 1977 Ralph Nader's health branch of Public Citizen (the Health Research Group) released a fascinating report with a long title: "Why Not the Most? A Physician's Guide to Locating in Cities with the Most Excessive Medicare Fees in the Country and an HEW Guide to Stopping This Waste of a Billion Dollars." The study, headed by Ted Bogue, a lawyer, found very wide differences in the fees charged to Medicare patients for four common operations in thirty-nine different localities studied.

After adjusting for the difference in the cost of living in different communities, they still found that the cost of each of the four operations was three times as high in the highest fee areas as in the lowest ones. For example, the fee-adjusted cost of a gallbladder removal ranged from $813 in Manhattan and $626 in the Bronx and Brooklyn, to $476 in Washington, $413 in Philadelphia, and $242 in Scott County, Minnesota. While the ophthalmologists in rural Nebraska were only getting $375 for removing a cataract, those in Beverly Hills were getting $1,000, even though the cost of living was only 11 percent higher there.

Dr. Sidney M. Wolfe, director of the Health Research Group, charged that it was costing the Medicare program and the patients (who pay 20 percent of the fees) at least $1 billion extra for these regional differences in fees. The report said it found no correlation between the fees charged and either the quality of service provided or the shortage of physicians in the area.

About a week after this report came out, the *New York Times* in a tongue-in-cheek editorial, "The Flying Gall Bladder," said a Manhattan resident could fly to Findlay, Ohio, have his gallbladder removed there, see a little of the country, return home, and still save $528. The cost of the gallbladder operation in Manhattan was $1,000, 245 percent higher than the Findlay charge of $290, even though it only cost 37 percent more to live in Manhattan. Or, the editorial pointed out, one could pay for round trip air fare from Orange County, California, to Buffalo, have a prostatectomy there, and still come out $89 ahead.

The federal government had found similar erratic charges a year earlier but did not release much of the information for fear that doctors with lower fees might increase theirs. While it found that two-thirds of the fees clustered around the average, some fees varied by a factor of 5 or 6. For example, breast operations varied from $175 in one locality to $1,200 in another. One type of prostate operation varied from $200 to $1,000, even though the average was $500. And some tests varied even more. Cystoscopies, instrument examinations of the urinary tract, varied from $7.50 to $125; hemoglobin tests from $1 to $18; and electrocardiograms from $5 to $75. On the average, they found specialists charged more than GPs.

While doctors' wide variance in fees cannot be rationally explained, their high fees are of concern to citizens, employers, health insurers, and the federal government, which is paying for a growing proportion of medical care. Doctors generally appear to be in a seller's market. Their fees have kept substantially ahead of the rise in the cost of living nearly every year since Medicare went into operation in 1965. And their incomes have also outdistanced the cost of living increases. In 1975 general surgeons' net income went up 14.5 percent, to a median of $83,270, in comparison to a 7.0 percent rise in the consumer price index. In 1975 the incomes of general surgeons were exceeded by obstetrician-gynecologists, whose median income was $83,390. In that year they earned 17 percent more than internists and 41 percent more than general practitioners.

And these statistics do not tell the whole story, for they include M.D.s who are still in residency practice, most of whom are earning under $20,000 per year. While the median net earnings of obstetricians and gynecologists was $83,390 in 1975, 42 percent reported earnings of $80,000 or more—some much more. For the first couple of years of practice, some surgeons may have low incomes, especially where there is an oversupply of them. But Dr. Edgar Berman, author of *The Solid Gold Stethoscope,* said: "I have a relative in a major city, a surgeon who's been out five years and makes $175,000 a year. There are professors who both teach and practice, making $400,000 and $500,000. In Maryland there was one pathologist who recently made more than $400,000 a year and another who made $300,000. . . . But the thing is, there is no doctor who isn't going to live not only well but luxuriously practicing honestly. And yet there's so much corruption in medicine." To illustrate this, he pointed out that the Moss subcommittee, invesitgating Medicaid and Medicare fraud, showed "that $2 billion was ripped off in a year from Medicare. . . ."

If there is an oversupply of surgeons, and there surely is, one might think that surgeons would compete for business and that this would then drive down the price of surgery. Many surgeons do compete for business, but by kicking back part of the fee to the referring doctor. This is called fee splitting, and we shall look at it in a minute. But while it does occur, it does not lower surgical fees; in fact, it may raise them. Then why are surgical fees relatively high in comparison to other physicians' fees or for the amount of time a surgeon spends on a case?

There may be several reasons for it, although some are more a matter of tradition than of logic. One reason is that competition requires informed buyers. They must not only know if they need a service but what is a fair price for it. Those are two things patients generally lack. First of all, not understanding medicine, they "must rely upon the doctor to determine how much and what kinds of medical treatment they require," in the words of Erwin Blackstone, an economist. He continues, "The surgeon is thus in a position to suggest that unnecessary work be done." Or as a physician states it: "Every specialty has its guaranteed income operation. The protologist has his hemorrhoids. The nose and throat man has his tonsils. The general surgeon has his appendix and gall-bladder. The neurosurgeon has his disk. The gynecologist has his uterus and ovaries. You can go on and on." Theoretically, at least, surgeons can create their own demand if they are so inclined.

The second thing a patient needs to have, for competition to work, is the price of an item or a service. But both physicians and lawyers forbid price competition. While doctors do not compete on the basis of price, which is one thing patients could understand, they may compete on the basis of quality, which most patients are ill-equipped to fathom. In fact, there may be a certain snob appeal in surgery. Those who can pay more may be willing to pay more, using the higher fee as an index to quality. But whether a higher fee is a good index to quality surgery is doubtful. Nevertheless, this "price discrimination" may in turn be the reason that so many physicians are attracted to this specialty that we now find loaded to surplus. They in turn need to do more surgery or charge more for it to be satisfied.

Another reason why patients do not look into the relative price of surgery is the nature of the doctor-patient relationship. The surgeon is seen as much more of a personal friend and a trusted professional than a department store clerk. Patients are embarrassed talking about a fee, and so are many doctors. It is part of the "medical mystique" which sometimes insulates doctors from an equal encounter with patients. Neither wants to initiate the discussion. The doctor rarely tells the patient his fee for fear that the patient might think it is the uppermost consideration in his mind. And the patient hates to raise the question for the same reason—he thinks it might be offensive to suggest that money is one of the reasons the doctor is providing the care.

Several other elements may enter into the lack of examination of fees. One is that it often comes at a critical time in a person's life—when he is sick. At such times patients are not in the mood for bargain hunting and would not want to go to the added time and probably expense to find a "better buy." And one usually wants the "best" in health care, "regardless of cost." Furthermore, doctors do not openly advertise and are usually reluctant even to give office fee schedules, let alone surgical fees, to consumer advocates who want them for a brochure on physicians' services.

One other factor undoubtedly contributes to patients' lack of interest in comparing surgical fees—insurance. Having already paid a hefty premium, or seeing it as a covered fringe benefit, many insured patients no longer worry much about the surgeon's fee. Since in most cases he may pay only a small portion of the fee out-of-pocket, it appears as a "benefit" which smart shopping would little change. On the other hand, the large and growing number of people insured for hospital care has probably contributed to both high fees and unnecessary surgery. Covered by insurance for all or most of the cost of an operation and hospital costs, a patient has little economic deterrent to undergoing elective surgery. And most companies will pay the "usual and customary" fees for surgery. This tends to translate into what the highest-priced surgeon is charging in a particular community, and thus other surgeons keep elevating their fees to the highest. Some surgeons, knowing that the insurance company will pay $600 for a certain operation, may tack on another $200, justifying the decision by saying that the patient's out-of-pocket cost is "only $200."

While surgeons average about 20 percent more income than other specialists, and most could earn even more if they were quite busy in surgery, how do they justify their higher incomes? They usually argue that their training is longer than most specialists', that it takes longer to get started in practice, that the demands of surgery are greater, and that they must also assume more responsibility for the patients' well being than those giving shots and pills. Not only that, their malpractice premiums are higher, they are under greater threat for malpractice liability, and their average work life is shorter because of the physical and psychological demands of surgery.

Patients rarely get to see how doctors feel about fees. Some of Marcia Millman's observations of how doctors feels about fees came from her two-year period of observing and listening to doctors as reported in her book *The Unkindest Cut.* She reports as follows on a conversation (typical?) between two doctors fictitiously named Lerner and Johnson:

As they waited together for another hour to see how the patient was doing, the two physicians commiserated about how difficult it was to collect payments from Medicaid, and how they felt that Blue Cross–Blue Shield payment schedules discriminated against medical doctors in favor of surgeons. In their view, while surgeons were paid large fees by the insurance companies for a suture job that took only ten minutes, as medical doctors they were paid only small fees for diagnosing a problem... which could take several hours of their time. Internists, who generally considered themselves to be the "intellectuals" of medicine, frequently joked that surgeons were the dumb "plumbers" or "technicians" of their trade. But this feeling of superiority did not compensate the internists sufficiently for what they believed to be unfair differences in salaries and earnings. Lerner felt especially irritated about the payment schedules of the insurance companies, for he had many cardiac cases and would often have to spend hours diagnosing and evaluating a heart attack, and a surgeon could earn in twenty minutes the amount of money that

Lerner might be paid for a night's work. Lerner and Johnson then discussed the fact that many cardiologists were beginning to administer unnecessary and expensive diagnostic tests because these tests only took a small amount of the doctor's time and brought in a good fee for the doctor from the insurance companies. Many doctors felt that it was one of the few opportunities they had to collect fees approaching those allotted to surgeons.

Whether the high fees of surgeons are justified is one important question; but another important question is whether fees should be split between the referring physician and the surgeon doing the operating. As we indicated earlier, fee splitting is one way surplus surgeons compete for business—by offering some split, or a better split of the fee than some other surgeon, to the referring doctor. The way it works is this. Dr. X— say, an internist or GP—works out an arrangement with Dr. Y, the surgeon. For each surgical patient referred to him whom he operates on, Dr. Y gives Dr. X a certain portion of his fee—maybe 10 percent or up to 50 percent. Or he may give him gifts. In this way Dr. Y may ensure surgical patients coming to him.

Since 1918 fee splitting has been condemned. In its most recent statement of principles, the American College of Surgeons says, "A surgeon must refuse to divide fees, directly or indirectly." It says violation of this principle will "disqualify an application" or be a "cause for expulsion" from membership in the college. It explains: "Any form of inducement to refer a patient to another physician, other than the superior care to be secured, is unethical. Fee splitting is one form of unethical inducement." So are indirect inducements, whether they be bribes, gifts, or whatever.

One can easily see how fee splitting could lead to inferior care. Prompted by financial payoffs, the referring physician might send a patient not necessarily to the best surgeon but to the one who gives him any or the biggest kickback. And knowing he would get a kickback for referring surgical patients, he might look for such patients.

Naturally, if there were not a surplus of surgeons competing for patients among themselves and with GPs who do surgery, then there would be no fee splitting. The very existence of fee splitting suggests we have too many doctors doing surgery.

How extensive is fee splitting? Nobody knows, because it is one of those unethical forms of conduct where the victim, the patient, is almost always unaware of it. And since it is also illegal in federal law and none of the states approve while about half explicitly forbid it, the doctors who practice it usually conceal it. "The attack on fee-splitting was initiated by the American College of Surgeons, with only partial success. Reformers were confronted with a surreptitious breach of ethics, difficult to uncover, impossible to eradicate," states the SOSSUS report.

Fee splitting has been condemned by the AMA, but little effective action has been undertaken to eradicate it. When Dr. Paul R. Hawley, director of the American College of Surgeons in the 1950s, said that the AMA's resolutions meant nothing, and went directly to the American public to explain the evil nature of fee splitting, the AMA's House of Delegates saw eleven resolutions of censure introduced, but not against fee splitting. They were introduced to censure him, according to William Michelfelder, because Hawley had discussed fee splitting in a magazine which reached thousands of Americans.

In 1970 *Medical Economics* said: "The fact remains that even in Chicago, the home city of the American College of Surgeons and the American Medical Association, fee-splitting is rampant. Few young surgeons in Chicago would dream of starting practice without being fully prepared to split fees." Dr. Alex Gerber said not a single voice of protest was made following this statement in one of the most widely circulated journals doctors take. Dr. Nolen tells of a fellow surgeon who began practicing in a New England city of 50,000 but "didn't do very well. There were more surgeons in the city than were needed and there was a lot of fee-splitting going on. There was also a lot of surgery being done for reasons [he] considered something less than valid."

In *A Surgeon's World* Dr. Nolen gives an insider's view of how fee splitting works, the ways doctors technically get around it, the taboo, and the rationalizations they develop to justify this. But before I report on that, I must first briefly describe "itinerant surgery" and tell why the American College of Surgeons proscribes it. Itinerant surgery occurs when a physician from another town or city comes to do elective surgery without first making the preoperative determination that the surgery is needed and/or appropriate and without offering the postoperative care. Sometimes it occurs in small hospitals where no surgeon is on the staff. A surgeon from a nearby town or university is called in to do only the surgery instead of the patient being sent to that surgeon's hospital. Often a local hospital does not want to "lose" money by having its patients go to another hospital. Surgeons believe that they can better determine the need for surgery and offer better care after it than can nonsurgeons.

However, the American College of Surgeons says that some emergency surgery may have to be done on an itinerant basis, but that it should not be habitually done. They also say postoperative care can be delegated to "another physician as well qualified"—meaning another surgeon. Itinerant surgery often occurs with fee splitting. It all depends on how the doctors present their bills, as well as on any other transactions between the doctors. If the operating surgeon presents the full bill to patients but rebates part of it to a local physician for the pre- and post-operative care, then we have fee splitting. But if each doctor independently presents his bill for his part in caring for the patient, then everything is above-board.

When Dr. Nolen first moved to Litchfield, Minnesota, in 1960, he was the first surgeon on the staff of the Meeker County Hospital, with 97 beds serving about 19,000 residents. Part of the reason he chose this community was that there was no surgeon there. He had visited a number of other communities in other states and found them discouraging him from coming either because there was already a surplus of surgeons or because the general practitioners did the surgery and did not want the competition of a better qualified doctor. Consequently Dr. Nolen felt he could keep busy as a surgeon in Litchfield. But at the end of the first year about the only surgery he was doing was emergency surgery, and that usually at night. Finally he talked to one of his fellow doctors, a GP, about why he was not getting any referrals. The explanation was a twofold economic one.

First, the GPs in this community felt that if they referred patients to Nolen for surgery they might lose them to him for other purposes—that is, for primary care. Many United States surgeons are not sufficiently busy in surgery, and so they do offer some primary care: everything from treating colds to heart pain to keep busy.

The second reason was that an itinerant surgeon from Minneapolis drove out to Litchfield to do most of the elective surgery. And he usually charged only half his fee so that the referring physician, who gave the pre- and post-operative care, could collect the other half from the patients. To get elective surgical work, Nolen agreed then to use the referring doctor as a "consultant" and split the fee, in a technically acceptable way, by presenting separate bills. Nolen said, "I'll go along. When I do the case you provide the pre- and post-operative care with one stipulation: if I think that it's the kind of case where I ought to give the patient regular personal attention after surgery, then I'll do it and charge for it...."

So, with the money problem resolved, I started getting the referrals." The itinerant surgeon never operated in Litchfield again.

Dr. Nolen thinks too much is made of fee splitting and its evils. It certainly can be evil if the referring doctor chooses surgeons solely on the basis of the kickback and not on their competency! Sometimes the operating surgeon who uses GPs or internists for pre- and post-operative consultations with separate fees resorts to fee splitting to get around insurance companies. If insurers will only recognize the bill from one doctor—the operating surgeon and not the consulting doctor, physicians may resort to fee splitting so that the patient can get as much as he can from the insurer and pay as little as possible out of his own pocket.

Economists argue that fee splitting is largely the result of a surplus of surgeons competing for too few surgical patients. Dr. Nolen thinks there is another reason why fee splitting persists "despite repeated attempts to do away with it." Surgeons are highly paid for what they do, and GPs, internists and other nonoperating doctors resent it. They think they should get a bigger bite out of the patient's dollar. They have a point." Nolen then seems to go on to say that fee splitting is a way, perhaps a legitimate one, to redistribute the overly high fees of surgeons to other doctors. He admits surgeons' fees are high and vary greatly across the country. And rather than arguing for lowering them or making them more uniform, he seems to approve of questionable ways of redistributing them so that nonsurgeons can share in them and keep the referrals coming.

Another practice in American medicine that draws criticism is "ghost surgery." Most of it now takes place in teaching hospitals that have surgical residency programs. There it is probably common, but in private practice in nonteaching hospitals it may be relatively rare. Because it involves deception of the patient, the strictures against it are quite unenforceable.

Ghost surgery is really fee splitting in reverse. The patient is led to believe by the doctor he went to that he will perform the surgery. But after the patient is anesthetized the "ghost doctor" comes into the operating room, does the surgery, and leaves before the patient awakens. The bill is submitted by the doctor who is believed by the patient to have done the surgery. He then splits the fee in some fashion with the ghost surgeon, who remains unknown to the patient or his family.

This type of ghost surgery is probably relatively rare today because it is fraudulent and hard to conceal. The patient has not given his consent to have an unknown surgeon of unknown ability operate on him. The practice may not only result in a form of fee splitting but could tempt the hiring physician to choose doctors who will operate for less money while the hiring physician submits a big bill. Because nurses and anesthetists know who is doing the operating and this is often put on a patient's chart, it is harder to conceal in nonteaching hospitals.

But there is another form of ghost surgery that occurs in many teaching hospitals, of which there are hundreds. The case of—we shall call her Nancy Cameron—illustrates this well. She told two reporters, Toby Cohen and Marshall N. Levin, that she had had a mastectomy. She said, "I picked what I thought was the best doctor around and paid him a very steep fee—$1,500 out of my own pocket." She said she wanted a "good job of surgery," so she chose a doctor with a "superb reputation" who left minimal scars. But, she reports, "I ended up looking like I was sewn up by a local tailor. I had gone to this doctor because he was noted for the unobtrusive scars he left, and I wound up with a scar so grotesque it's unbelievable."

She continued, "I found out later that he didn't do any part of the operation." By chance she looked at her hospital chart at the nurses' station and saw another physician's name. "I confronted my doctor with this and he said the other doctor, the resident, only did a very small part of the operation. And he sort of bawled me out for reading my own chart."

Then she saw an attorney, who subpoenaed the records, which revealed that her doctor had not done any part of the operation. In Nancy Cameron's words, "He merely supervised."

Is this unusual? Not at all. In residency training programs residents assist in many operations. Fairly early in their training career they do simple operations, like appendices, under supervision. Later they progress to more complex surgery, first under supervision, then sometimes without it.

From all the evidence, this form of ghost surgery is not uncommon. In the four to five years of training, each of some twelve thousand surgical residents will individually perform in the neighborhood of five hundred operations, besides assisting in even more. All residents collectively probably perform at least a million operations a year.

All this may come as no surprise. How do surgeons learn to become surgeons? They learn by practicing on patients. What patients? Before the introduction of Medicaid and Medicare, they got a lot of their experience from operating on "charity" patients—those who were wards of a public hospital because they could not afford a private doctor. But with the introduction of these federal programs and a more widely insured population, charity patients have been greatly reduced, although Medicaid patients are still considered "teaching patients."

That relief recipients are still used as teaching material came to light in 1975 when the Massachusetts Welfare Commissioner Jerald L. Stevens charged that he had clear evidence that hospitals in that state were providing unnecessary surgery to general relief recipients. He said, "We have material to suggest that in some cases a large number of appendectomies were performed on what appear to have been healthy appendixes." He went on to clarify: "However, the surgery may have been justified in most of those cases on the basis of the preliminary diagnosis. It also may not have been." Appearing with Mike Wallace on CBS-TV's "Sixty Minutes," Stevens also charged that general relief patients were being used by residents and interns for practice in teaching hospitals. Furthermore, he pointed out that because the charges at teaching hospitals were higher than at other hospitals, he questioned "whether it is sound practice to admit publicly assisted patients to high cost facilities when comparable care is available less expensively."

But Medicaid patients are not always numerous enough, nor do they present the variety of surgical problems that good "teaching and practice" require. Thus, residents gain much of their surgical residence on "private patients," the patients of attending doctors. While the attending doctor may do part of the surgery, allowing the residents only to "open and close" the patients, sometimes they only supervise and sometimes not even that. "In the better educational programs, the residents do all the surgery. All the surgery," says Dr. Terry Cardin, an emergency room physician in Chicago's Highland Park Hospital. Dr. Sheldon Rosenthal of New York reports, "As a resident, I did prostatectomies on private patients by myself. I did nephrectomies (kidney removals). I once did a radical rectopubic prostatectomy without anyone around."

According to Dr. Frederick V. Lorenzo, a resident at the University of Pittsburgh's Presbyterian Hospital, "In our institution we get to do quite a lot of operating in the five years of our training program. A lot of the surgeons seem to be willing to let the residents do a significant number of their private cases."

The critical question is not whether residents gain their experience by operating on either "public" or private patients. One of the critical questions is whether patients know this. The other question is whether the patients are any worse for it.

The answer to the first question is that many patients, like Nancy Cameron, do not know it. Toby Cohen and Marshall Levin report, "A random survey of more than 100 post-operative patients at major medical complexes in Philadelphia and New York City failed to turn up even one who had been told—either before their operation or after—of any resident participation in the surgery." They emphasize, "This despite the fact that physicians at these hospitals freely admit residents participate in most surgery."

On Sunday, March 13, 1977, the "Sixty Minutes" program of CBS pointed out that much surgery at some hospitals is done by residents and not the private doctor the patient thinks is doing it. Usually patients sign a long consent form that says they give their consent for the operation to the surgeon or "his designatee." But few ever read the fine print or think to ask what "designatee" means. It means the resident. In the particular case they described, the resident did the surgery. The next week "Sixty Minutes" reported that the hospital where this occurred claimed they were engaged in no wrongdoing, but they said that thereafter when residents would be doing the surgery patients would be fully notified.

Whether patients are specifically informed about who is doing the surgery appears to vary by hospital and by physician. One physician from Massachusetts General Hospital, when asked if patients were told about residents' participation, replied: "I think that's asking for trouble. I have no qualms at all about telling patients exactly what's going to happen, but I don't go out of my way to raise questions in their mind that didn't exist before." Another doctor said, "Well, you don't want to scare a patient to death. I might not tell a patient because I don't want to frighten him."

In contrast, Dr. Judah Folkman, surgeon-in-chief at Boston's famed Children's Hospital, will not tolerate any form of ghost surgery. "I will always introduce the resident and say he's going to help me operate. If we have to keep something a secret, we shouldn't be doing it. If you think it's unethical and you must keep it a secret, you have no business doing it at all."

Different people, including patients, react differently to such deception as that which is involved in resident ghost surgery. Some feel that it is a breach of honesty not to inform the patient fully, that it involves a situation to which a patient has not given his informed consent. Others feel that such deception is not important. What is important to them may be satisfactory surgery (to the patient) and a good training program (for the physicians). Dr. Hooter, professor of surgery at Columbia Presbyterian, points out: "The attending surgeon, even if he's merely supervisory, is still fully responsible for anything that happens. Although residents operating on private patients without their knowledge implies a form of dishonesty, the reason I don't tell patients as a routine is because some people are unwilling to grasp the concept that residents are fully capable of performing good surgery under supervision." But how does he know ahead of time which patients can grasp this idea?

Is this belief in good surgery justified? In many cases I am sure it is. The supervising surgeon is the brain, the judgment; the resident, the hands. But Dr. William Nolen's reports of residents' errors in judgment about patients, sometimes unsupervised, in *The Making of a Surgeon,* is rather scary. His report of the first operation he performed and then later of younger residents under him is rather frightening. He bumbled through his first appendectomy by cutting too deeply, forgetting how to tie knots to seal off bleeding blood vessels, having to search for the appendix, and cutting incorrectly. The operation took two hours, exposing the patient to more anesthesia than usual for this normally quick operation. Dr. Nolen reports the man did recover but "not without a long and complicated convalescence. His bowel refused to function normally for two weeks and he became enormously distended."

I do not know how others feel about it, but I should like to know about the skills of somebody operating on me. If I am paying for it, I do not want to be practiced on. At the same time practice must occur in training residents. Does the doctor know best if he hides this from the patient?

The provision of medical and surgical care under fee-for-service arrangements creates other problems as well. Competitions for patients does not reduce the costs of services, and it often leads to jurisdictional disputes over who should be operating on what part of the body. Ronald Kotulak of the *Chicago Tribune* asked Dr. Edgar Berman, "Do the various specialists jealously guard their territories?" Berman replied:

Very much so. There's a gerrymandering of the body. The gastrointestinal surgeon wants to do the esophagus while the chestman says, "That's in the chest; I should be doing the esophagus." The nose and throat man says, "Well, the entrance of the esophagus is in the throat; I should be doing that." Breast specialists say, "I should be doing the breast," while the general surgeon says, "I know more about the breast than you do." The gynecologist says, "This is in a female; I should be doing the breast."

When Dr. Nolen first practiced at a private hospital, he became aware, he said, "for the first time, of the intense economic competition between the various surgical specialists. The gynecologists, the thoracic surgeons, the pediatric surgeons, the protologists—all the subspecialists—fought like tigers to protect their respective domains from infringement by outsiders." And, "No one bucked the system," because that impaired referrals and cooperation. While the system was ostensibly developed to ensure that each patient got the doctor most appropriate for his condition, Nolen found at that private hospital it "was enforced rigidly and unreasonably, not for the protection of the patient, but for the protection of the specialists who were in greater supply than the demand warranted. They had to protect their narrow domains to ensure themselves of healthy incomes." Because of this, patients got more runarounds from doctors, having to see several when one would have done, or having operations by two different specialists when one could have done it. The result of this controlled competition in some instances is that the patient has to pay more.

In summary, fees and the fee system create a number of problems in American medicine: high, erratic, and inflationary charges, the questionable use of fees as an index to quality of care, unethical fee splitting, ghost surgery, jurisdictional disputes over the human body that may raise the cost of medical care and restrain cooperative patient management. And not least, surgery may be sold to unwary patients. With a surplus of surgeons, especially general surgeons, they need either to do more surgery or charge higher prices for it to achieve the lifestyle they expect surgeons should have. The result is apparently more surgery at a higher cost than we need or than is beneficial.

While there are some good points to be made about fee practice, it does appear to lead to more unnecessary surgery. That fees are important factors in contributing to unnecessary surgery came to light in one study carried out by Dr. Paul Lembcke, a professor of public health and preventive medicine at UCLA's School of Public Health. He found in one hospital audit that when an all-specialist medical staff was paid salaries, the gynecologists did about 26 hysterectomies per audit period. But later, when a fee-for-service reward system was developed, they did 130 hysterectomies per audit period.

The fact that salaried physicians in health maintenance organizations do substantially less elective surgery—sometimes 30 to 40 percent less— with no apparent detriment to the health of their patients is rather substantial evidence that some kinds of surgical care are overutilized. Dr. Alfred Bauer says that HMOs using salaried doctors have shown that you need only about one-half the hospital beds when "the profit motive is eliminated" from medicine.

Dr. Avedis Donabedian, professor of medical care organization at the University of Michigan, argues that good medical care is discouraged by the fee-for-service system, because under it doctors make money if they see more patients and do more operations. To remove the profiteering in medicine, Dr. Bonnell Boardman argues we need to *"take the financial incentive out of the piecework practice of surgery and medicine."* (Emphasis in original.)

11

CHANGING PEOPLE: PLASTIC SURGERY

Plastic surgeons have not and will not let a good thing like cosmetic surgery pass them by. Medicine has done beautifully so far by catering to the patient's fears and pain what but a windfall it'll be cashing in on their vanity. [Edgar Berman, M.D.]

Plastic surgery covers the whole human body. It ranges from correcting cleft palates and the removal of warts to nose bobs and hair implants. In a society that fears aging and worships its movie stars, it is no surprise that one wing of plastic surgery, cosmetic surgery, is one of the growth areas in American medicine. Dr. Thomas Baker, a plastic surgeon, did ten facelifts in 1959 when he opened up practice in Miami, one of the centers for cosmetic surgery. In 1977 he and his two colleagues expected they would do 350 facelifts. While some physicians are respected, plastic surgeons, like hairdressers, are often adored. And a few women visit them for nips and tucks as often as they do their gynecologists for periodic checkups.

Cosmetic surgeons do not come cheaply. The results of most surgery are hidden from view; but the results of cosmetic surgery are there to be seen by the world. In the words of the world's leading cosmetic surgeon, Dr. Ivo Pitanguz of Rio de Janeiro, who caters to the jet setters, cosmetic surgery is the "most creative branch" of surgery. For $1,500 to $3,000 wrinkled skin and sagging jowls can be tightened. A vertical incision is made in the temple region in front of the ear and then back up behind the ear on each side of the head. The skin is lifted and "undermined" with a scalpel to separate it from fat and muscle underneath and then stretched taut on both sides until wrinkles and pouches disappear. Excessive skin is trimmed away and sutured neatly around the ears.

But cosmetic surgeons are not limited to changing wrinkled, baggy skin. For about $1,200 puffy fat around the eyes can be removed, for around $1,500 busts can be enlarged, reduced, made more pointed or rounded according to the proclivities of the wife (or husband). And for up to $5,000 "full body contours" can be undertaken to remove the fat from ungainly hips, thighs, and stomach.

Now that movie stars and politicians openly admit their cosmetic surgery, it will face a wide-open future. Just how many people are there who like their profiles or their physiques? Where appearances are so important, cosmetic surgery has come of age. "Like cancer surgery, it's no longer taboo," says Dr. Franklin Ashley of the University of California at Los Angeles. "Now people talk openly about having a facelift or breast reconstruction, just as they would about a cancer operation." Phyllis Diller makes comic relief out of her facelift, eye de-bagging, and breast reconstruction. While cosmetic surgery seems most prevalent at the top of the social ladder, it too may have to be made available to all. Yesterday's luxury may be tomorrow's necessity.

Vanity surgery would always appear to be unnecessary surgery. But here again we come across that term "unnecessary" that varies by the person doing the defining. To say it is necessary in the sense of simply enabling one to live would probably eliminate all of it. But there is more to life than mere existence. People want quality too, and the quality of a person's appearance is important, at least to some people. And the quality of appearance can sometimes be improved by sanding off warts, lifting drooping buttocks, reducing bulbous noses, or expanding miniature bust lines.

Plastic surgery began in ancient India to repair the amputated ears, noses, and other parts marked on criminals and female adulterers. Today it is often associated in the public mind with repairing the markings of age and ethnicity. Frances Cooke Macgregor did an interesting study of eighty-nine people who had "nose jobs" by intensively interviewing them before the operation about their background and the reasons they wanted the operation. While their motives were often hidden, lengthy interviews revealed two types. One type was made up of "changers" who felt they had an "ethnic nose" and wanted it changed to avoid discrimination, teasing, and stereotyping. Most prominent among the ethnic groups were

Greeks and Armenian Jews who had armenoid noses, characterized as long, convex, downward sloping noses with depressed tips and thick flared wings. They felt they could be "more American," more beautiful, and could better get jobs and dates if they did not have a "Jewish" nose.

The other group was characterized as the "fixers." These were the ones with ugly noses—too long, too big, flat, bulbous, twisted, hinged, hooked, disproportionate, or convex. They wanted to overcome the evil or tough personality characteristics associated with an ugly nose. They felt a cosmetic repair job would enable them to avoid the teasing epithets they had known for a lifetime—Little Moose, Banana Nose, Tomato Nose, Pinnocchio, Beak, the Hawk, Pug, Hook Nose, and Ski Snoot. After the operations they often reported they felt things went better for them and they liked themselves better.

But there is more to plastic surgery than turning an ethnic nose into an "American" one. While vanity surgery may be the growth area, reconstructive surgery to repair the defects of birth and accidents often seems more justifiable than sanding the skin a little smoother or changing facial features to appear more beautiful. Take the case of Ingrid DeValery. She was born in Finland. Her father had considerable wealth and was known in business circles for his strong convictions, his intolerance for failure, and his keen business skills. Ingrid took after her father much more than after her mother, who was interested in the social life that accompanied their upper class status. Ingrid was expected to be proficient in athletics, and was. Her schooling was spread over many European schools and tutors, as she was often on the move with her parents. At age thirteen, when her parents divorced, she spent some time in convents. But she could not adjust to the rules and transferred out of a second convent after being dismissed from the first one.

She was an active girl who was becoming a very beautiful woman. At seventeen she married, but divorced her husband when she found he was unfaithful. At age nineteen she moved to France with her only child, a son, and his nurse. She frequently dated a young man who wanted to marry her in spite of her refusals. One day she was riding with him in a car when it left the road. He was killed; Ingrid's body and her face were horribly damaged by the accident. She was hospitalized for two years. Both legs were severely fractured and she had multiple compound fractures of the facial bones. The middle section of her face had been pushed inward, leaving a vast distortion. Her upper lip was both elevated and pushed inward making occlusion of her lips impossible. Two unsightly folds marked each side of her nose, which was shortened and twisted. Her lower left eye lid sagged in the absence of a sustaining bone support, making the eye appear to protrude.

In the nearly two years Ingrid was in the hospital, she slowly became aware of her grotesque appearance. She was blind for nearly a year from the trauma, during which her head was enclosed in a cast up to her eyes. Unable to eat, she dropped from 150 to 60 pounds. She heard her nurses describe her face as "ruined." She felt inwardly dead as her friends said, in effect, "Poor Ingrid, how can you have the will to live in your pitiful condition?" As her vision returned slowly, she saw her own distorted face and yellowed teeth. During her nineteenth and twentieth years she underwent nineteen operations to reconstruct her jaw and teeth, but with limited improvement in her facial appearance.

Ingrid considered three alternatives: suicide, a convent where she wouldn't have to face the world, or "normal" life as an ugly woman. With the love and support of a French aristocrat to whom her distorted face meant little, she chose the third alternative.

Over the next ten years she underwent another thirty operations in France. While this reduced many of the distortions, she was called the "broken mug" in her home city. She coped well with the stigma that accompanies physical disfigurement. A man in a drugstore said to her one day, "We have hospitals and convalescent homes where people like you can go and where you can avoid being out in public." A waiter in a restaurant commented, "You are a great lady to go out in public with such a handicap. I could never do it." While tormented by the appearance that brought such comments, she refused defeat. "One can't give up. There is nothing else to do. You have to go on pretending you don't notice and never show you feel inferior."

She continued in a variety of business ventures with success, and then at the age of thirty-three came to New York for additional surgery. Over the next several years seventeen additional operations were performed, each requiring anywhere from two days to a week in the hospital. She wanted to wipe out the disfigurement. As time passed, Ingrid's facial appearance did improve greatly. Her left eye protrusion was corrected and her separated lips brought together. An acrylic support, inserted in her nasal cavity and supported by her upper denture, gave her nose a normal contour. After years of reconstructive work, dozens of anesthesias, and great pain and cost, her face was normal with the exception of her nose, where further improvement was seen as unlikely.

Was this surgery necessary? No, if we mean simply maintaining human existence. Even then we cannot rule out the possibility of suicide having been averted by the progress that was made in restoring her face. But it was vitally important to her—psychologically helpful if not actually necessary—to be able to cope with the cruelty that humans exhibit in the face of ugliness.

Ingrid's case reveals one type of plastic surgery, reconstructive surgery. Reconstructive surgery refers to those "operations undertaken to correct, as far as possible, the face or other parts of the body that are distorted or maimed as a result of congenital anomalies, disease, or trauma." Reconstructive surgery is vitally important to many. The burn victim who has been disfigured by scars or the person born with a cleft palate would not consider it unnecessary or trivial. Neither would the war casualty whose face was badly marred by a hand grenade.

But the other type of plastic surgery, "cosmetic surgery," raises questions about how important or necessary it is, who should pay for it, and who decides when and if it should be done. Cosmetic surgery involves "improving" the appearance of "normal" individuals. True, our standards of what is beautiful are highly influenced by culture. We do not think the Papuans' practice of inserting sticks in the nasal septum makes them more attractive. Nor do we find the extension of African lips with disks beautifying as portrayed in the *National Geographic*. Beauty is not only culture-specific but time-specific. We no longer go in for plump cheeks, dueling scars, powdered wigs, or wrinkled hands and faces.

Cosmetic surgery is a growth industry in the United States. While a lot of people are not totally pleased with their appearances, only recently have surgical cures been offered for this. For centuries, and according to the fashion of the times, people have dieted, worn constraining corsets, painted their eyes, cheeks, lips, fingernails, and toenails, clipped, burned, shaved, pulled, and dyed the hair on their head, face, eyebrows or wherever it may grow on the human body. But cosmetic surgery, from nose jobs (rhinoplasties) to silicone injections, has come of age. Both the general public and most physicians have recently legitimated cosmetic surgery. Twenty-five years ago both men and women tried to hide their identity if they had resorted to surgery to change the shape of their nose, chin, lips, or ears. Men were considered vain to want such things done to them, but no longer. In 1949 only about 15,000 cosmetic operations were undertaken; today about a million operations are suffered through to improve the contours of noses, jowls, busts, and bottoms. In a competitive job market oriented to youth, some physicial obsolescence can be hidden if baggy eyes or jowls, double chins and bald heads can be corrected.

While most cosmetic surgery is considered minor, there is risk with all surgery—anesthesia, cutting, possible infection, and always some pain. And then there is disappointment: the convex nose that becomes too concave to have the cute curl; the presence of some sagging in the jowls and lower eyelids despite the facelift. Yet people are voluntarily asking and paying for the opportunities to have a new face.

But the question then arises, who should pay for reconstructive surgery, or cosmetic surgery, or the surgery that falls in the gray area between these two categories? If we eventually have some form of national health insurance, should cosmetic surgery for a facelift be as available to the scrubwoman as to the elite dowager? But if not, would we not be returning to a two-level system of medical care—one for the haves and one for the have-nots?

In a modified form this question recently came up in Massachusetts. In March of 1977 Massachusetts Blue Cross–Blue Shield announced that as of July 1 that year it would no longer pay for breast reconstruction following a mastectomy unless the group plan purchased a special rider for its enrollees. It said it was paying anywhere from $650 to $6,500 per case, depending on how extensive the procedure was and when it was done. However, at no time did Blue Cross–Blue Shield cancel coverage for a breast prosthesis worn in brassieres and costing about one-half the amount of a simple implant done on an out-patient basis.

The announcement led to a storm of protest from plastic surgeons who do breast reconstruction as well as from many women and women's groups. It also revealed that there were differences among cancer physicians about the appropriateness and timing of the reconstruction. One plastic surgeon called the rider option a fraud and said that its use was a way for Blue Cross–Blue Shield to save face "while women go on losing their breasts." Some of the women's groups which protested the move said the ruling was discriminatory toward women and chauvinistic. Another physician said the decision was economically motivated and "unquestionably discriminatory."

Part of the controversy centered on differences in medical opinion about the timing of the implant. Blue Cross–Blue Shield contended that breast implants led to infection in 45 percent of the cases. But prominent plastic surgeons said that complications occur in only about five cases out of a hundred. In rechecking its figures, Blue Cross–Blue Shield said it found only an 8 percent infection rate if the implant was done in a separate operation several months after the mastectomy, but 37 percent if done simultaneously with the operation.

Mainly as a result of the deluge of protest from women, on June 1, 1977, a month before the exclusion was to go into effect, Massachusetts Blue Cross-Blue Shield announced that it had reversed its earlier decision and would continue to pay for the costs of breast reconstruction. But the plan said it did not favor the operation under certain conditions—where there were signs that some cancer still existed or where the cancer was a "large, unfavorable growth."

This controversy points up the difficulty of assessing what is "necessary" surgery, for there are often economic, medical, and social-psychological components. The economic approach often finds such surgery questionable because it has few ways to measure the benefits in dollar terms. Medically, the operation may be more or less justifiable, depending on how the woman feels about it and on her age and total medical condition. And socially and psychologically, "for a lot of women," says Dr. Peter Mozden of the Boston University Medical Center, "loss of the breast is a crushing blow." He feels that the fear of the permanent loss of a breast truly dissuades some women from going for a breast cancer checkup as much as does the fear of cancer itself.

While the fear of loss of a breast or the loss of a breast itself must by psychologically upsetting to women, the stigma that attaches itself to people who are abnormal in appearance, especially in the face, may be even more psychologically disturbing. Dr. Frances Macgregor says that facial disfigurement is "one of the most devastating of social handicaps." While an ugly appearance or a facial deformity may leave no actual impairment in carrying out normal human behavior, as does a physical handicap, the reactions of others may greatly hinder a person from accepting himself and relating to others in a normal way. Disfigured people often must suffer through stares, remarks, curiosity, questionings, pity, rejection, ridicule, nicknames, whispering, and outright discrimination.

Dr. Macgregor, in *Transformation and Identity: The Face and Plastic Surgery*, gives many extended examples of the psychological trauma that develops as a result of facial disfigurement from congenital defects, disease, or accidents. Suffering individuals develop a variety of techniques to deal with the thoughtless stereotyping of other people: total seclusion, avoidance of many social contacts, depression and shame requiring professional help, suicide, or exaggerated aggression. It is not easy to develop a healthy way to deal with the avoidance, stares, teasing, qu80tioning, and dioorimination that go along with having a doviant faco.

Take the case of Charlotte B., age thirty-six, who suffered chronically from suppurative frontal sinusitis (an inflammation of the mucous membrane in her forehead). A radical operation involved removing a large portion of the frontal bone in her forehead, which resulted in a deep and conspicuous depression in the middle of her forehead and a scar across her nose. Upon seeing herself in the mirror following the surgery, she was so distressed that she cried for two days. She felt she was so "repulsive" she would not let friends visit her in the hospital. Upon returning to her stenographic job, she found her self-confidence further undermined by stares and questions in the elevator, her office, the street, and buses. Formerly sociable and outgoing, now she refused to go anywhere because she could not stand the staring and the questions. She avoided eye contact with others to avoid conversations. She wept often, became depressed, and began taking barbiturates to deal with her anxiety.

After a few months recovery from her operation and the reduction of the swelling in her forehead, she was eligible for plastic surgery. But she needed extra money for the operation. When she applied for waitressing jobs to supplement her regular income, she was always turned down. "They would look at my face and say they had no position available." She became semihysterical in her self-pity. Her grooming habits declined. She became fearful she might lose her job because she could no longer concentrate.

Finally Charlotte underwent reconstruction of her frontal bone by grafts removed from her ilium. The results were highly successful. In three weeks her face appeared normal except for a slight scar. Her expression became radiant, and her untidy and drab appearance were dramatically changed. "I've been a different person since this operation. It's as though I had gone to sleep and awakened as somebody else. I look in the mirror and grin from ear to ear and spend hours looking at myself," Charlotte said. "Before, I couldn't bear to see myself. Everyone is amazed at the physical and mental change in me and I feel relieved of a great weight." She reported going out again and not crying any more and being "glad to get up in the mornings."

Thousands of people are scarred from burns, automobile and job accidents, and the ravages of disease. Some can be helped, often dramatically, others cannot, by reconstructive plastic surgery. While their surgery may be more "justifiable" than cosmetic surgery, how does one determine what is important or valuable? As long as the individual makes the decision and pays for it, there is no real problem in justifying any plastic surgery. But if the patient's surgery is paid for by group insurance plans, be they federal or private, where should the line be drawn if at all? How can an outsider evaluate the psychological benefits that the straightening of a nose or the addition of a prosthetic ear absent before birth may have?

Perhaps the problem of determining what is necessary or justifiable surgery reaches its zenith in sex change surgery. Such surgery presents a tangle of medical, legal, and social issues; it also stirs disbelief if not moral repugnance in most people.

Transsexuals are those who consider themselves members of the opposite sex; they are not to be confused with transvestites, who dress like the opposite sex but do not consider themselves members of it. Transsexuals, while physically normal, find a discomfort in their gender at an early age, as a rule. They usually "feel" like a member of the opposite sex, desire to dress and act like a member of the opposite sex, and, after "sex reassignment surgery," are usually attracted to members of their original sex. In this way they are different from homosexuals, who have sexual desires for members of the same sex, and from bisexuals, who have sexual desires for members of both sexes.

About 80 percent of those who both want and finally receive a sex change operation are males who want to be converted to females. But those desiring the female-to-male operation confront a greater problem in getting successful surgery, according to Dr. John Money of the Gender Identity Clinic of the Johns Hopkins Medical Center in Baltimore. He does not recommend the construction of a penis, a phaloplasty; but most have a double mastectomy to get what looks cosmetically like a male breast. However, about half the women who desire a sex change operation do want a penis even though it may take as many as fifteen hospital stays to develop either a urinary tube or a copulatory tube or both from the gracilis muscle of the upper thigh and abdominal skin grafts. But often the results are not totally pleasing aesthetically and even less so in performance.

The male-to-female operation is less costly and often yields better results. While breast enlargements may be accomplished by hormones or surgery, the main project involves excising the body of the penis and folding its skin inward to line a vaginal cavity which first has been created in the musculature of the perineum. The scrotum is used to construct a labia, and the urethra is shortened so that it will come out in the right place in the blind-end vagina. According to one surgeon, such vagina-plastics are believable, allow patients to provide male partners with gratifying sex, and sometimes yield orgasms for the person who has had the operation.

Now, if the person pays for the operation(s) himself, and it costs anywhere from $5,000 to $10,000 for hospitalization and surgery, there may be no problem in saying the surgery is justifiable in the patient's mind. But apparently few surgeons recommend it; most realize that it provides no miraculous change, and they weed out about three-quarters of those who want the operation. They always point out that the surgery is irreversible and results in infertility. But should public funds—either federal or commercial, or private nonprofit funds—be used to pay the costs of such surgery? Herbert Black reports that Blue Cross–Blue Shield will usually reimburse much of the expense of the operation.

While these operations are technically possible and usually yield physiologically satisfactory results, are they psychologically and socially beneficial? Not always. Doctors at the Gender Identity Clinic of the Johns Hopkins Medical Center try to weed out most candidates by careful prescreening. Psychiatrists often suggest that candidates for the operation take opposite sex hormones for a period of time preceding the operation (also after it, should they have it) and try out the opposite sex role for at least six months to determine if they really want it.

In this period the males take estrogen, which develops their breasts, softens skin texture, and redistributes body weight. But it does not change body hair or the pitch of the voice. Some men who take the hormone and try to pass as women in this period find that coping with the female role with a male face, body, and voice is too difficult. They cannot pass for the attractive woman they feel like. Female transsexuals take androgens, which stop menstruation, increase sex drive, and stimulate the growth of body hair. Sometimes they can adjust, sometimes not. But going through such a testing period often gives them a taste of the complicated social changes and adaptations they would have to go through if they had the operation.

Dr. Jon Meyer says he has changed his mind on the origin of trans-sexualism. While at one time he believed it was the unfolding of a natural predisposition, now he believes it is the result of "childhood deprivation." He prefers psychiatriac therapy to the irreversible surgery route. While some doctors believe that counseling should be first tried, they believe that only surgery will help some individuals resolve their identity crisis. Even then the patients may face psychological and social problems in living with a new identity among curious and skeptical persons. Like homosexuals who decide to keep their sexual persuasion no longer a secret, transsexuals usually must go through the trauma of telling parents, friends, and employers of their change. To avoid repercussions they may move to a different location to start a new life.

In many ways transsexual surgery is more like cosmetic surgery than reconstructive surgery. Both seem to be concerned with changing an identity with which the individual is not satisfied. But whereas the cosmetic operation tries to improve a relatively normal condition, the sex-change surgery tries to change a normal physiological condition that does not coincide with a psychological condition of identifying with the opposite sex. The therapeutic approach says the individual's "abnormal" psyche should be altered to square with his body, while the surgical approach alters the body to coincide with the person's feelings. Which is the best approach? There may be no blanket answers.

As in other controversial issues discussed in this book, there is wide-ranging opinion, but often insufficient evidence on which to base a sound conclusion. Better evidence is needed on the degree to which and in what ways transsexual surgery is beneficial to those individuals who have it in comparison to those who might benefit from it but instead opt for or, out of financial necessity, get, therapeutic or no treatment. While such evidence might be helpful in personal and societal decision making on the justification for that kind of surgery, it does not answer some of the larger social questions. These include such questions as whether more of our personal and national resources should be put into education or military defense or roads or industrial capitalization or housing and nutrition. While most of these are political decisions that must be hammered out in the crucible of public debate, many of the "medical" questions remain in a medical establishment where it is assumed the doctor knows best.

12

CORONARY ARTERY BYPASS SURGERY: SOME QUESTIONS

The manner in which coronary bypass surgery developed in the United States reflects the laissez-faire attitudes and structures that characterize American medicine. Two facts are central in this matter. First, there are no restrictions on how experimental surgical procedures can be used in American medicine. Second, although there is some indication that specialists within surgery may soon try to exclude less specialized general surgeons from dipping into their areas of practice, it is generally the case that surgeons loyally support one another in resisting any regulation or restriction on surgical practice. [Marcia Millman]

We were in agreement that the eventual answer could not and would not be surgery. Surgery was not only too expensive but it didn't get at the root of the problem, prevention of the development of arteriosclerosis. [William Nolen]

From the point of view of society's resource allocation, however, coronary bypass surgery appears less attractive. . . . What is optimal medical care for the individual patient may not be optimal when we, as society collectively, consider what it is costing us. [Milton C. Weinstein, Joseph S. Pliskin, and William B. Stason]

Each year about one and one-half million people have heart attacks—either angina (pain from the heart getting an insufficient supply of blood) or an infarct (a segment of the heart muscle dies because it has been deprived of a sufficient blood supply). Around half of them will die, but the other half, about 700,000, will live but in fear of another heart attack that might be fatal. Some of those who survive, perhaps a quarter of them—around 150,000—*might* benefit from the operation known as coronary artery bypass surgery. The cost in the United States at $12,000 per operation would be $1,800,000,000. Is it worth it?

The answer to this question is not fully known yet because coronary bypass surgery is a relatively new surgical technique that is sweeping the country but whose benefits and costs are not fully measured or understood. Furthermore, as we shall see, it depends on your point of view. Your point of view may be different if you are a patient experiencing angina with your life under threat from what it would be if you were healthy but concerned about rising premiums for health insurance and public funds being used for very expensive operations. And the patient or citizen view may be different from that of the surgeon and anesthesiologist whose major incomes come from heart surgery.

Coronary artery disease is now better understood than it was years ago. Coronary artery disease occurs when obstruction (arteriosclerotic plaque) builds up in one or more of the two arteries (the right and the left, which subdivide into the left main, circumflex, and left anterior arteries) which supply the blood to the heart. These obstructions or occlusions are either partial (say 70 percent or 90 percent) or total. They typically give rise to angina (heart pain), especially under stress or exertion, and may lead to infarcts (heart attacks) where a portion of the heart dies from a lack of blood. About one half of the infarcts are so damaging that they cause death.

But until 1959 there was no way to know which or how many of the arteries were obstructed or the degree of obstruction. In that year Dr. Mason Sones of the Cleveland Clinic developed a technique called the angiogram. This technique involves inserting a small, hollow plastic tube called a catheter into an artery in the arm and threading it under x-ray visualization into the heart and the various mouths of the coronary arteries. These arteries are slightly smaller than the size of drinking straws at their openings and get smaller as they descend around the heart. Dye is then injected into each of the coronary arteries, and x-ray pictures are taken and carefully examined to determine how much, if any, obstruction exists in the various arteries. It is necessary to determine where the arteries are blocked and the extent of their blockage so that the surgeon will know which of the arteries need to be bypassed in his operation.

The surgery itself involves cutting the patient open to the bone along the length of the breastbone, sawing through the entire length of the sternum, cranking the chest open with a metal spreader and then opening the pericardium—a thin sac which surrounds the heart. While this is being done, another surgeon will be opening the thigh in order to remove a superficial saphenous vein to be used as the bypass artery or arteries (anywhere from one to nine bypasses may be used). This vein is usually cut into a number of about five- to ten-inch pieces. These pieces are then sewn to the aorta artery just above the places where the right and left coronary arteries originate.

Next the patient will be put on the heart lung machine. This must be done to stop the heart from beating so that the saphenous vein bypasses can be sewn to the coronary arteries below the point of the obstruction. It would be very difficult to do the delicate sewing necessary if the heart were quivering at its regular pulse. Yet the heart muscle must not be stopped too long or it will begin to die. The patient is connected to the heart lung machine by means of two plastic tubes, one connected to the aorta and the other to the right atrium which receives blood from the rest of the body. Without blood flowing through it, the heart stops beating. While the heart is still, other repairs may be made to it such as cutting away dead tissue or putting in new valves. After the vein grafts have been sewn in place, the heart lung machine is turned off and blood begins flowing into the heart. Often it does not begin beating by itself, so the surgeon will shock it with two paddles—plastic-covered electric stimulators. Usually it starts the heart beating again. After making sure there are no leaks and after measuring the amount of flow in the new bypasses to determine how well they are working, the surgeon will close the openings made for the heart lung machine. The chest will be closed, using wire sutures to pull together the two halves of the sternum.

Barring numerous possible complications during the angiogram, surgery, and recovery period, the patient often feels better and can lead a more active life after the operation. In a minute I will return to some of the major risks associated with this surgery.

Let us return to the original question: Is is worth it? Essentially, the goals for a patient willing to undergo the costs and risks of the operation are three. The first is to relieve angina pectoris, or chest pain, and simultaneously to allow the patient to tolerate more activity and exercise. Here the operation is beneficial in most cases. In 75 to 85 percent of the cases patients report no, or substantially less, pain than before the operation. Many can return to swimming, golf, tennis, or physically demanding work without the pain they had before. The quality of their life is improved to a greater extent, in fact more than double, than if the operation were merely a placebo. Patients are usually enthusiastic about the operation because they can live a less sedentary life without chest pain or the fear of it. Apparently the bypass arteries do supply the heart with more blood, at least for a while.

The second goal is to prevent heart attacks and the deterioration of the heart muscle that would occur if the obstruction in the arteries continued (which it would) and/or progressed. And the third goal is related to the second one—the prolongation of life. On both these latter goals the early evidence is rather mixed and unclear, partly because the results have not really been subjected to the kind of scientific testing called clinical trials. Coronary bypass surgery was not begun until 1967 and not performed very widely until the early 1970s. Furthermore, while studies are now underway to determine if patients who have the surgery live longer or have fewer heart attacks while alive than comparable patients who do not have the surgery, the results are not in on this yet.

Results from some of the studies done to date are tentative and sometimes conflicting. No strong evidence exists yet that such surgery either prevents heart attacks or prolongs life. It may, but perhaps for only a minority of patients—those with several arteries severely obstructed. Some early evidence suggested that the operation may damage the heart and that plaque builds up in the bypasses as fast or faster than in the original arteries. Furthermore, there is a tendency among laymen to confuse relief of pain with an actual cure for coronary disease, which by its nature is a progressive chronic one.

Marcia Millman has recently reviewed the evidence on the effectiveness of coronary bypass surgery. She makes three major points: (1) "There is a great discrepancy between what patients believe about the operation's efficacy and what has actually been scientifically demonstrated." We shall look at this evidence first. (2) "The operation has been developed and applied in a completely unregulated fashion: often to the detriment of the patients undergoing the procedure." The evidence is that many surgeons and hospitals have been involved in the fad to get open-heart surgery suites and equipment. But there is considerable variation in their "success" in terms of patient survival and complications. (3) The cost of this "high technology" operation is extensively paid for by the public, with the profits going to large corporations involved in the health industry, hospitals, and the surgical teams involved.

Millman's first point is that many patients believe they are cured by the operation even though the major evidence so far is that they only have their angina relieved and exercise tolerance extended. Still, this is an important gain. But as to the question of prolonging life or reducing heart attacks, the medical profession presents disagreement. Some patients have a heart attack during the angiography, the surgery, or soon afterward, resulting in dead tissue which no longer gives rise to pain. Thus, the reduction of the pain following surgery may be attributed to the placebo effect, (more) dead tissue in the heart, or greater blood flow to the heart. Where exercise tolerance is improved, however, the evidence suggests it is at least partly attributable to the greater blood flow. But the use of a medical approach involving drugs such as Propanolol has often been effective in reducing pain in 65 to 95 percent of all cases, although the relief is not always as great as with surgery. But neither is the cost or risk as great, as we shall see shortly. Furthermore, there is evidence that in many of those who have surgery the pain returns slowly over a period of years.

Does the operation prolong life and prevent future heart attacks? The early evidence says it depends on a number of things, mainly on the overall health of the patient and the particular nature of the coronary artery disease of the patient. It appears that it usually extends life for those who are relatively young and in good health otherwise, who have not had a heart attack yet nor congestive heart failure, but who do experience angina in normal activities that are not highly strenuous and who have multiple artery obstruction. But for many others the evidence is subject to the clinical judgment and conservative or liberal interpretation of the physician making it.

The cost of the operation now varies from about $10,000 to $25,000, depending on who does it, hospital charges, length of stay, and complications. The average charge is probably in the neighborhood of $12,000 and rising at about 10 percent a year. While the majority have their angina reduced, about 10 to 20 percent do not. As many as 10 to 25 percent have a heart attack during or soon after surgery even though one of the goals is to eliminate it. It may postpone attacks for some patients, but this is largely an unknown. There is considerable evidence that the bypassed arteries have an accelerated deterioration, and that the new bypass arteries often become occluded over several years, both of which may lead to heart attacks. And, of course, about 10 percent of all patients die during or soon after surgery. This depends on the health of the patient as well as the skill and experience of the surgeons.

There are variations among the rates of those surviving, depending on their overall health when they enter the operation as well as on the quality of the surgical team doing the operation. One in one hundred to two hundred patients will die during the angiogram preceding the operation, which may trigger a myocardial infarction; but the rate varies from .5 percent in a good hospital up to 5 percent in a poor one. The good hospital is characterized in this instance by extensive experience in the procedure. Hospitals performing fewer than 100 coronary arteriograms a year have five times as many deaths, heart attacks, and cerebral embolisms as hospitals that do more than 400 a year.

The number of people who die from surgery or complications varies greatly according to the experience of those operating and the overall health and age of those having this procedure done. With growing experience in the operation, the overall mortality rate is decreasing. But here again the mortality rate can be "interpreted." If the operating team is operating on patients in fairly good health, with minimal coronary artery disease, and then in only one artery, their chances of survival may be 99 in 100. But if it is done on elderly patients who already have extensive heart damage and obstructions in two or more arteries, their chances of surviving may be much lower—maybe 95 or 75 in 100.

Marcia Millman contends that many patients are sold on this surgery by the mass media, which report spectacular results by the use of "selective statistics" from doctors, or by the surgeon who is going to undertake the operation. "Patients are misled," she contends, "not only because they are told the most promising statistics, but also because they are *not* told of the many risks and limitations of the operation." Sometimes the pressure to do the surgery may come from highly optimistic patients; but, contends Millman, "It is probably more typical that badly informed patients are influenced by the enthusiasm of physicians who often present it as a lifesaving device." Millman reports one patient who said to her: "'The doctor said I really didn't have a choice. That if I didn't have the operation I probably wouldn't be around next Christmas.'"

One research cardiologist told Millman that in "his opinion . . . 80 percent of the bypass operations being done are worthless apart from temporarily relieving symptoms, and he added that many well-informed physicians shared his judgment." But he told her that most doctors will not say much about it in public because the overall success of the operation has been neither proved nor disproved and that therefore it is a "sensitive area" in medicine. On the other hand, one cardiologist

I talked to felt it reduced heart attacks and extended the life of about 80 percent of the patients undergoing the operation.

Dr. Christian Barnard, the South African surgeon who performed the first heart transplant, made a point at a recent medical meeting about why physicians are reluctant to say much that is critical about this operation: "There is no other operation in the treatment of heart disease more misused than coronary artery surgery. The first reason is that it's good money. You can earn a lot as a coronary artery surgeon. Second, it's a very easy operation technically, and in many cases the patients do well even if you don't do anything. I would predict that if coronary artery surgery were made illegal in the world today, half the heart surgeons would be out of business and would have to beg for their money, because they exist on this type of surgery."

And it is a big business. Annually there are around 70,000 coronary bypass operations being performed in the United States, and if recent trends continue it may expand to over 100,000 a year or more. Marcia Millman contends it has developed in an unregulated way because it is popular with surgeons, hospitals, and the hospital supply industry. Generally, good surgeons at good hospitals lose only 2 patients in 100 within thirty days after the surgery. But in a minute we shall see that there are many exceptions to this.

Because bypass surgery looked like a good thing, many surgeons began doing the operation and many hospitals bought the equipment necessary for it. The Inter-Society Commission for Heart Disease Resources developed guidelines about the resources (equipment, personnel, and minimum case loads) hospitals should have to do the operation. One of these guidelines was that a hospital should do two hundred of these operations a year in order to maintain the skills of the operating team. Despite these "guidelines" most hospitals and surgeons that wanted to do the operation kept on doing it even if they did not have the minimum caseload. In 1969 only 5 percent, or 25 out of 480, hospitals met these guidelines: more recently only 15 percent of the hospitals were meeting the guidelines. Who pays for this unregulated overdevelopment of coronary bypass surgery suites and operating teams? Both individual patients and the public which supports hospitals through federal grants, insurance payments, and fees.

Take the case of Malden Hospital in Massachusetts, where 51 percent of the patients undergoing open heart surgery between 1968 and 1975 did not survive. While many physicians in the area knew of this very high mortality rate, they did nothing about it except to refer their cardiac cases to physicians at other hospitals. Both the surgeons operating there got many of their referrals from some distance away or out of state. According to the reporter Richard Knox, the situation came to light in 1975 because David Rosenberg, a hospital cardiac technician, "complained to state authorities because he could not stand by and watch more patients undergo open heart surgery by members of the [Cardiothoracic Associates] group."

The eight surgeon members of Cardiothoracic Associates lost 33 out of 64 open heart surgery patients at Malden Hospital—a mortality rate six to ten times that of experienced centers where such surgery was performed. Doing surgery there from 1969, they averaged only 11 such operations a year over the six-year period—far below the 200 believed to be necessary to maintain skills. And this same group of surgeons lost over 22 percent of 288 open heart surgery patients operated upon from 1972 through 1975 at nearby Mt. Auburn Hospital in Cambridge, the only other hospital where they did this type of surgery. There they were averaging about 70 heart surgery operations a year, some of them bypass operations.

Members of this surgical group defended their high mortality rate by saying they were operating on only the highest risk patients and that the Malden Hospital accepted more such patients than other hospitals. But one cardiac surgeon who supervises a large number of open heart surgeries said, "I couldn't pick a group of patients at this [my] hospital to come up with a mortality experience that high." And another thoracic surgeon, who supervises five to six open heart operations weekly, said: "Fifty percent represents an extremely high mortality for these procedures. I don't think even 12 percent is justifiable today, though it may have been five or six years ago." Massachusetts General Hospital, which performs more than 1,000 open heart procedures a year, has a mortality rate of only 13 to 15 percent for the highest risk patients (those with severe chest pain while at rest, who require aortic valve replacement, multiple coronary artery bypass grafts, replacement of a previously operated mitral valve, or correction of a gross congenital anatomical defect). Dr. Richard Mamiya, a mainland trained, third generation Japanese Hawaiian, has performed 350 consecutive bypass operations without a death at Honolulu's Queen's and Straub hospitals.

After the publicity about the high mortality rate from open heart surgery performed by Cardiothoracic Associates, the group resigned its cardiac surgery privileges at the Mt. Auburn Hospital in Cambridge. One of the senior members of the group resigned from the presidency of the American College of Cardiology on the eve of his installation, saying that adverse personal publicity might reflect on the college.

Following the complaint of David Rosenberg, the Massachusetts Department of Public Health began a review of the Malden Hospital mortality rate of 51 percent. They asked the American Association for Thoracic Surgery to perform independently a case-by-case review of the open heart surgery at the Malden Hospital. But before they got an independent review by several leading heart surgeons, Malden Hospital had to agree to pay all costs as well as all legal fees and possible damages if lawsuits were initiated by physicians whose performance was being reviewed.

The issue of legal risk stemmed from a 1975–76 case in which the Arizona Board of Medical Examiners hired an independent group of surgeons to investigate whether an Arizona heart surgeon, Dr. Edward Diethrich, was responsible for unjustified heart surgery and excessive surgical mortality rates. This independent panel criticized Dr. Diethrich "for performing heart surgery 'without apparent medical necessity' and for mortality rates 'substantially and alarmingly above the accepted norm.'" The medical review panel said Diethrich's mortality rate was 25 percent for aortic valve replacements and 30 percent for mitral valve replacements. Diethrich then filed a $135-million restraint-of-trade suit against nine doctors for filing "an inaccurate and purposely deceptive report" with the state medical examiners. He charged them with a conspiracy to damage his reputation and restrain the trade of cardiovascular surgery.

In April, 1976, a committee of three physicians appointed by the American Association for Thoracic Surgery reviewed all pertinent data to evaluate the Malden Hospital open heart surgical program. They concluded that the hospital's high death rate in these cases did "not compare favorably" with averages at other hospitals. (It was about ten times higher.) They said they were of the "opinion that the surgical team had insufficient experience in cardiovascular surgery requiring extracorporeal support" which resulted in "excessive operating times and a high incidence of peri-operative complications" and thereby a high mortality rate. They were also of the opinion that some of the critically ill patients operated on at the Malden Hospital "should have been transferred to a center more active in open heart surgery." They also criticized the inadequacy of the autopsy pathology reports and the superficiality of the mortality conferences following such deaths. They argued that had such information been used other deaths might have been prevented. In late 1977 Richard Knox reported that the Massachusetts medical discipline board planned to hold an investigatory conference with the eight surgeons in Cardiothoracic Associates. The Massachusetts board was apparently considering using a new power delegated to it—the power to limit a doctor's license rather than revoke or suspend it. This meant they could find physicians incompetent to do some procedures but not generally incompetent. This case could result in a landmark decision limiting the practice rights of physicians.

I do not know how many hospitals have as poor a track record in open heart surgery as that of Malden Hospital. But there may be more since a majority of hospitals where this surgery is performed do not meet the guidelines for this type of surgery. For example, in 1971 over 52 percent of the hospitals doing this kind of surgery were doing less than 100 a year, compared to the 200 cases generally seen as a minimum number to maintain team operating skills. By contrast, the eight members of the Cardiothoracic Associates performed only 56 to 64 such operations at Malden Hospital over eight years and a total of about 200 in all hospitals where they did such procedures. Thus, they were averaging only about 25 cases a year—far below the minimum.

The recent expansion of hospitals and surgeons doing this kind of surgery, however, illustrates what Millman calls "laissez-faire in American surgical experiments." She argues that incompetent surgical teams continue to get referrals for this operation and that their track records are not given to patients so they can make important decisions about their own lives in an informed way. Generally, regulation has not been effective in limiting who does such surgery or where it is done. The recent Malden Hospital situation illustrates this. While members of the medical profession often know that some places do have poor survival rates, they are slow to act because of the complex legal, economic, and medical politics involved.

When Herbert Denenberg, former insurance commissioner of Pennsylvania, tried to develop a contract with Blue Cross–Blue Shield to phase out heart surgery programs in that state which fell below the guidelines, he was unable to do so because of the resistance of local doctors. His reasoning in trying to do this was twofold. One reason was that some of the surgical teams were not performing enough of the operations to maintain their skills. Another reason was that the hospitals offering the unnecessary programs had to raise the daily hospital rates for all patients, sometimes by as much as ten dollars a day per patient, to pay for the equipment and resources needed for it, for an open heart surgery suite may cost $250,000 or more.

In their 1975 report the Intersociety Commission for Heart Disease Resources said:

Within the past three decades cardiac surgical teams have been organized throughout the United States. Some have failed because of poor planning, inadequate staff and lack of material resources. Others have had case loads so marginal as to raise serious questions about their effectiveness, safety and economic soundness. Even today the majority of cardiac surgery programs appear to be operating well below capacity. . . .

The overexpansion of many hospital surgical programs to do open heart surgery has been profitable to the electronic industries who produce expensive diagnostic or monitoring equipment like the heart lung machines used in the operation. And it has opened up new vistas for an oversupply of thoracic surgeons. Some heart surgery like that done on congenital malformations for a very small and stable segment of the population, is limited; "by contrast, surgery for coronary artery disease. . . involves no such delimited population," writes Dr. Francis Moore, a surgeon. "In this country and in Western Europe coronary artery disease may be important in as many as 30 percent of the male population reaching the age of 55. . . . The potential need for cardiac surgery and its populational potential are very impressive."

Millman argues:

It is not surprising that where there is an incentive to find surgical cases, the indications for surgery became looser. Thus many physicians have informally observed (but without wishing to be quoted) that in areas of the country with large numbers of private community hospitals and a high concentration of cardiac surgeons, bypass operations are more likely to be performed with questionable indications.

She continues by pointing out that bypass surgery is less frequent in countries with a "smaller ratio of thoracic surgeons to population" than the United States, or in health maintenance organizations where cardiologists and surgeons are salaried. She concludes that "all of these facts suggest that what is seen as an 'indication' for surgery is not based merely or primarily upon scientific evidence but also on the basis of the financial incentives of those who make the judgments."

Coronary artery bypass graft surgery has developed in a rather un-regulated way and probably has been overperformed. Such surgery rests on complex clinical judgments where it is often difficult to carry out carefully controlled studies. Should patients be assigned to a "medical" group or a surgical treatment group if there is a very small probability that the length or quality of their life might be improved, by a small increment, by surgery? Should the patient have the right to decide to which group he should be assigned? Or might he simply have the surgical or medical treatment elsewhere if his assignment did not coincide with his choice? These are some of the complex ethical and administrative problems in developing and carrying out carefully controlled studies. Furthermore, even if or when better information is available from con-trolled studies, this does not mean that either physicians or patients will know about it or use it if it conflicts with their interests and desires.

One leading cardiac surgeon, who remains anonymous, was asked why there were not earlier controlled studies of bypass surgery and why any hospital could do it even if they did not meet the guidelines for the surgery. His candid reply was, "Well, you could say that we sacrifice people, and some people die, but people are dying off like flies anyway. They're dying from heart attacks in the millions. And you could say that there are too many people anyway."

When asked why there were no controls to ensure that only qualified surgeons do the operation, he took a long-run view that seemed to justify sacrificing people in the short run. He said, "Eventually everything will balance out so that the incompetent doctors get driven out of the market. In coronary surgery you find out when patients die because of incom-petence—there are too many people involved for the surgeon's mistakes to go unnoticed." Then he pointed out that with a gallbladder operation, perhaps undertaken without an x-ray, only the doctor and the operating room nurse know the results. Or "with a stomach operation you can go an inch too far in either direction and nothing will happen, but in coronary bypass surgery you can't." It is more technically demanding, and since more people are involved, "eventually your results will become obvious and you won't get any more referrals. . . . Eventually things will balance out. Rigid controls are no good. We have the best medical care system because it's competitive."

I for one would not want to be one of those patients who are sacrificed so that eventually incompetent surgeons are weeded out of this surgical field. Dr. Robert Replogle, an eminent cardiac surgeon at the University of Chicago Medical Center, believes that getting a second opinion in this area is vital. He says, "Very often a patient comes to me with a heart problem and says, 'Doc, I think you're a great guy, I love you, but I'd like to have a second opinion.' I always say to myself, 'This guy is smart.'"

Dr. Replogle also bluntly urges patients to ask the heart surgeon, "What's your track record?" Since buyers need to be aware in medicine as in other areas of the quality of services or goods they are buying, that is probably good advice.

But now that so much of the funding for heart surgery, or for all medical care for that matter, no longer comes out of the individual's pocket, the larger societal issue is whether the extensive resources necessary for it are justified. In a cost-benefit analysis Weinstein, Pliskin, and Stason argue that bypass surgery in many cases does not appear "optimal." Or as Millman argues, "But since we have only a finite amount of resources to spend on health care, what is necessary or unnecessary surgery must be publicly decided and viewed in terms of what best serves the entire society as well as what serves individuals." In her opinion:

It *is* clear that many patients who have had the operation should not have had it, or are unlikely to benefit from it. More careful testing at the beginning before the operation was given widespread application might have saved many patients from surgery we would consider "unnecessary" even by traditional definition. . . . More careful regulation of who may perform the operation and under what indications and circumstances might also eliminate some questionable practice of the surgery.

But the problem must be set in an even larger context. Should large sums of money be spent on such a procedure when comparable sums might add more life· years to our population if they were spent on reducing deaths from accidents or on preventive medicine in the field of anti-smoking clinics and low cost diet clinics? Perhaps, in the words of Millman, "we must think of what is necessary for the public good as well as what is necessary for some individuals" (patients and doctors). Rick J. Carlson in *The End of Medicine*, Ivan Illich in *Medical Nemesis*, and Dr. Jerrold S. Maxmen in *The Post-Physician Era* have raised the question of whether we are getting our money's worth in all areas from a largely autonomous medical profession which keeps elevating nondiseases and marginal diseases into new illnesses treated by a technologically oriented body of specialists at high costs. Have we created a medical culture that feeds upon the body but whose helpfulness is often marginal?

13

POSTSCRIPT: ON IMPROVING HONESTY AND QUALITY IN SURGICAL CARE

In my writing about medicine I have been considerably influenced by Dr. William Nolen, a surgeon who is also an excellent storyteller. One of the reasons he is excellent is because he tells the truth about his own practice and that of other doctors and surgeons. But one of the truthful things he tells is upsetting: doctors lie to patients to cover up their own mistakes, and they lie to patients to cover up the mistakes that other doctors make, to ensure that they will get referrals from them or so they can continue as friends and cooperative colleagues.

And while I understand it, I have difficulty accepting it as right. As Dr. Nolen says, "The system stifles self-criticism." By that he means that the fee system to a considerable extent is built upon interlocking referral patterns in which doctors will lose referrals if they knock other doctors either to their face or to the patients. "If you want a thriving practice," he says, "keep your mouth shut." Working as the sole surgeon in his community, he can be honest in describing cases of bungled surgery or surgeons working beyond their skill levels by keeping the cases anonymous. But, he points out, if he lived "in a wealthy suburb, competing with a multitude of other surgeons, I too might be afraid to speak out. That's the way the system works."

After observing doctors for two years in daily practice, Marcia Millman came to much the same conclusion as Nolen did. She writes in *The Unkindest Cut:* "There are two kinds of information that doctors routinely withhold from patients: one kind has to do with facts about the patient's illness; the other kind has to do with evaluations of the competence or performance of the other doctors involved in the case, or the wisdom of the treatment that other doctors have recommended." On the first kind of information withheld, information about the patient's illness, she says doctors maintain a "party-line." They particularly do not want to tell patients about disagreements doctors have about the advisability of different procedures, for fear that this will upset the patient. But, she points out: "Although doctors rationalize withholding such information (of both sorts) on the grounds of 'protecting' the patient from upsetting information, in fact they are more precisely protecting themselves and their colleagues. For the less that patients know about the problems of their treatment and the faults or errors of their doctors, the less able they are to disagree or make trouble for their physicians." Thus, by minimizing the amount of information patients have about their problems or the doctors treating them, physicians maximize their power, autonomy, and safety.

Nolen gives numerous illustrations of how the protection of colleagues leads not only to deception of patients but sometimes to inferior care for patients. For example, a salesman that Dr. Nolen described as a "mild hypochondriac" told Nolen that he had had a pain in his chest for the last few days. When Nolen asked him if it was bad, he said it was "just sort of annoying." Nolen listened to his heart with a stethoscope, told the salesman he sounded all right, and commented, "Probably just a little neuritis. Don't worry about it."

A week later the salesman visited a fellow doctor of Nolen's who took the time to give him an electrocardiogram which showed he was having a coronary heart attack. The man ended up in the hospital for six weeks. Nolen reports the fellow doctor could have made him look bad because in retrospect they both knew the salesman's "coronary had started before I'd seen him. If I had ordered the EKG, I'd have made the diagnosis." But Nolen reported his colleague "protected me. He implied to [the salesman] that the coronary had started the day [the other doctor] saw him, that an EKG a week earlier would have been normal, that [the salesman] had had neuritis for a week, and then a heart attack. I was very grateful."

I do not know whether, if the salesman had had his condition detected a week earlier, he would have been better. Perhaps the patient was better off not knowing the truth. But once the principle that prevention of the detection of doctors' errors is established, where does one draw the line?

Dr. Nolen tells of another case, of a boy who was not responding to treatment for pneumonia by a doctor he calls "Joe." Finally Joe called him in, and Nolen decided the boy needed surgery for appendicitis, which diagnosis Joe had missed. The boy got the surgery immediately, and then Nolen told the parents the boy had two diseases—first pneumonia and then appendicitis. "What I'd told them was the truth, sort of. The boy did have both appendicitis and pneumonia. What I didn't tell them was that he had probably had appendicitis for at least three days," comments Nolen, "and there was no sense in suggesting that Joe had missed the diagnosis. It wouldn't do the family any good and would only hurt Joe. I knew he'd protect me if the roles were reversed and I'd missed some medical ailment."

Why do doctors sometimes deceive patients? Not only to save egos and preserve referrals, but to avoid possible malpractice suits. Nolen believes that large city surgeons who are in oversupply are more likely to criticize fellow surgeons to both referring doctors and patients in order to build up their own practices. Nolen comments, "Actually it's this sort of thing, one doctor knocking another to a patient, that starts a lot of malpractice suits. Plant the idea in a patient's mind that maybe he hasn't had the best possible treatment and off he goes to the lawyer." Nolen seems to imply that this is wrong when it only may be bad for the doctor.

Perhaps these illustrations make the point about deception of patients. They are probably borderline in terms of damage or unnecessary suffering to the patients, but full details are lacking. However, the next case, one of hundreds that could be given, illustrates how the quality of surgical care may be impaired by the "system" which protects the livelihood and egos of doctors. In explaining this case, Nolen first says, "Strangely enough, in the cases which really represent malpractice the guilty physician is rarely ever sued." He then proceeds to tell the case of Dr. Jack Nadler (fictitiously named), a GP who did surgery but who was described as "fast," "careless," and prone to tackle difficult surgery beyond the level of his competence. In taking out the gallbladder of a man Nolen calls Abe Riley, Dr. Nadler botched it. While he did get the gallbladder out, he missed two stones in the bile duct which led to complications, something that frequently happened to Dr. Nadler's patients. Then, with Nolen's help, the man was reoperated on to recover the two missing stones. He had two operations when he needed only one well done. And Nolen says, "For an older, more decrepit patient a second operation could have been fatal." And it "cost him an extra month of recuperation," and extra expense and suffering.

In *The Unkindest Cut* Marcia Millman has an entire section composed of three chapters under the lead banner, "Overlooking Medical Mistakes." She argues with convincing evidence that "at every stop and turn of medical work, there are built-in professional protections for the doctor against having to recognize and take responsibility for mistakes made on patients." The mistakes, sometimes serious ones, made by interns and residents are seen as part of the natural learning process and therefore as granting them a certain immunity from accountability that private doctors and staff physicians do not have. It is her argument that doctors define "medical mistakes" in such a way as largely to exonerate themselves from responsibility when they are made. If they are made, "doctors develop group techniques for justifying their errors and minimizing the appearance of injury to the patient." And/or they close ranks and keep the patient uninformed "in order to protect themselves and their common interests against lay outsiders."

Her rather devastating conclusion is:

All of this is to say that the ideas, rules and practices about mistakes among doctors are not determined by a universal standard of right and wrong, or good and bad medical practice, but rather emerge from the practical interests of each department, hierarchical rank, and specialty group as they go about their routine daily work. [As a result,] in many private teaching hospitals, the ambiguity about who has authority and responsibility for regulating the quality of care often allows incompetence to go unchecked.

While she may overstate the case, it certainly raises questions about the honesty of many doctor-patient relationships, especially if things go wrong.

In some hospitals, but most likely in teaching hospitals, doctors sometimes squabble over who has the authority for the care of a particular patient and how he should be managed. Conflicts sometimes arise among "house officers" (interns and residents), private "attending" doctors who admit their patients to the hospital, and "staff physicians"— employees of the hospital. Marcia Millman reports, "Most often these conflicts would indirectly get expressed in terms of the care of a patient, sometimes to the patient's serious injury. As the following case illustrates, when residents and interns are angry with a private doctor, they will often vent their frustrations on the patient, for lack of other opportunities to express their feelings."

The case Millman refers to involved a woman with a history of tuberculosis and a seizure disorder which had been controlled by drugs. She had been admitted by a private doctor who turned her care over to a staff neurologist. The neurologist ordered a long series of tests which took two weeks to perform, even though daily requests were made by an intern (house officer) for a muscle biopsy which he thought would prove the woman was on the wrong medication. Because the staff neurologist would not arrange for the muscle biopsy, "one of the house officers suspected that the neurologist was stalling to use up the maximum of two weeks of hospital visiting fees allowed him by the patient's insurance plan," according to Millman.

When the muscle biopsy was obtained, it did indicate the woman was on the wrong medication. However, before they could change her to a new medication, they needed a sputum test to determine if the woman's tuberculosis was still active, for if it were, the new medicine could aggravate it. To get back at the staff and private physicians who had kept them waiting, the house officers in turn now deliberately delayed getting the sputum tests for a few days because they "forgot" or kept "finding" more pressing duties.

"In the meantime, several more days had passed and the patient remained in the hospital, deliberately ignored by the resentful house officers, and having come no closer to starting a treatment. But because her Dilatin had been discontinued, early one morning she suffered from a seizure and fell to the ground." Millman reports that another patient found her on the floor in a "confused, stuporous" condition.

When the patient was finally brought out of this condition she was left with a face and scalp so badly bruised that she had to undergo tests for a possible skull fracture. The next day, despite orders that she be confined to bed, she could be seen staggering up and down the hospital corridor with black and blue eyes and a badly bruised head.

Millman then points out, "This illustration is not at all unusual in the sense that house officers and private doctors frequently squabble over tests as a way of exercising control."

Millman also reports on the treatment of a thirty-five-year-old female patient at one hospital. She had complained of abdominal pains to several physicians over a number of years. They told her her pains were only "functional" (psychological). They contended x-rays were unneeded. When her pain became worse, she went to the emergency room several nights in a row, only to be sent home with a mild tranquilizer. She shortly returned to a physician again, this time jaundiced, and he admitted her to the hospital immediately even though before he had felt it was unnecessary.

During an x-ray test at the hospital, her liver failed to release a visualizing dye as it should have done. The doctor told her she needed a liver biopsy immediately. He told her that he had done hundreds of them and never lost a patient, even though such a procedure carries a small risk. Yielding to the pressure from this doctor to do the procedure, she decided not to see a liver specialist as she had first contemplated in order to possibly avoid the biopsy. Her doctor told her the test might confirm that she could have a very serious disease—chronic active hepatitis.

The doctor performed the liver biopsy and told her it had been done well. And she experienced no pain with the procedure. Upon returning to her ward, she heard several other patients say they were to have the same procedure the next day, raising the suspicion that this was this doctor's "specialty."

Unable to get a report on the results of the test that night, she got medical books from an intern which described various kinds of hepatitis. She was stunned when she found out chronic active hepatitis had no cure and was often fatal within a few years. She was unable to reach her physician over the three-day Fourth of July weekend. And the various house officers and associates of her physician would not give her the results of the test, contending that only her physician could do this. She was upset that they would not tell her the results, and she was depressed because she thought she might be dying.

When the physician returned, he was vague about the biopsy results but reported that her new blood tests were normal. This meant she could have avoided the biopsy if she had waited a week as she first planned. The doctor told her she needed gallbladder surgery the next day. He told her that the biopsy of her liver showed nothing wrong with it.

After the gallbladder operation the patient was still upset about the biopsy results and why the doctors remained evasive about the results. She asked her doctor to let her see her medical chart, which was kept at the nurses' station. While her doctor discouraged her from seeing it, he said she could. But later he told the nurses not to let her see it. This made her even more suspicious and furious. Finally she got the chart after a second confrontation with the doctor and found that it said no analysis was made of the biopsy; the specimen was insufficient for diagnosis. This meant that the procedure had been a waste but that the entire medical staff had tried to hide from her the fact that the physician had goofed and that the doctor had deceived her by saying the test showed nothing wrong with her liver.

There are two major, but not mutually exclusive, ways to deal with such problems as patient deception and a system which practices it. One is the institution of salaries for physicians to do away with the "business" of medicine. The other is a tighter credentialing system of doctors as well as an ongoing review of their practices by both fellow physicians and laymen.

Let us take the second one first. As it now stands, individual doctors can still too extensively determine what procedures they think they are capable of doing. A GP can do complicated coronary bypass surgery if he has the gall and the hospital to do it in. Hospitals need to be more strictly regulated in terms of who can perform certain procedures in them. And all hospitals should be required to be accredited. The very idea of an unaccredited hospital run for profit or to enable unqualified doctors to maintain practices in it is anathema.

But in addition to having tightly enforced accreditation standards for all hospitals and a tighter credentialing system for doctors, we need ongoing assessments of the skills and knowledge of those whose careless practices may mean death or suffering. A number of mechanisms may be needed to implement this: periodic relicensure and recertification based upon both achievement in continuing medical education and practice skills; constant assessment of the competence of doctors by fellow physicians and informed laymen by means of such things as Professional Standards Review Organizations, and utilization and tissue audit committees. I doubt that such review mechanisms will be totally effective without the participation of laymen because of the self-protective nature of any work group, including doctors.

This is not to say this will be easy. Take the case of age-impaired surgeons. Dr. Timothy Curran, an otolaryngologist from Hartford, Connecticut, says, "Generally, nothing short of the grossest infraction cam bump a hospital attendant from the staff." He feels that, "As long as a surgeon can still stand up he's free to operate. And if advancing age leaves his skill somewhat less sharp than his scalpel, his colleagues often look the other way." He recognizes that something must be done not only to protect patients but also to protect doctors and hospitals from malpractice liability. But how to determine when an aging surgeon has become a threat to patients is no easy task. Important tasks, however, are rarely easy.

Another approach to the problem of unnecessary surgery and poor surgical care induced by the financial incentives of fees and the fear of losing paying patients from referring doctors if coverups are not maintained, is the use of salaries for doctors. Of course, most doctors would resist the use of salaries. Part of the reason is that most of them have grown up in a fee-based system so they are not practically familiar with how salaries would work. Most probably resist the idea for fear that they would make less money than on fees. They see salaried doctors in Health Maintenance Organizations averaging less income than many of them. But it is also an important factor that doctors have been indoctrinated into the free-enterprise ideology of medical practice which allies them more with business than with the salaried professions like teaching. They believe that fees for each service they provide lead to better care for the patient because the physician must please the patient to get him to return. They argue that the salaried surgeon with an assured income and a forty-hour week will not make these extra efforts to please his patients. And they may be right in many cases.

But I also believe there is another side to the story. Salaried doctors will not be involved in the potential evils of fee splitting—sending patients to the doctor with the biggest kickback rather than to the best M.D. I believe that there would be less patient deception (usually said to be for the patient's own good) and fewer coverups of blunders when physicians were no longer dependent upon referrals for their livelihoods.

Would there be a decline in the quality of medical care if physicians were salaried? Dr. Alfred Bauer does not think so.

That depends on how you define quality of care. If you mean spending 10 minutes discussing a stuffed nose and the advantages of blowing it, or 15 minutes analyzing the jealousy of a three-year-old following the arrival of a new sibling, then the quality of care will decline. But if quality means efficient, no nonsense care without unneeded laboratory work or surgery, rendered by secure doctors whose judgment is detached from financial pressures and the popularity contest on which success in private practice partly depends, then there may even be improvement in quality.

Dr. Bauer, for one, wants to dump private practice and replace it with a national health service served by a national health corps of doctors. This private practitioner with, in his words, "solid conservative credentials," believes enough changes have occurred in the last ten years "to have rendered private practice no longer desirable." He believes the Medicaid mills rifled with fraud should be "replaced by clinics with salaried staff—again at great savings to taxpayers." He argues that health maintenance organizations have shown that surgery and hospitalization and hospital beds can be reduced when the profit motive is eliminated from medical care.

However, he thinks that about 10 percent of all physicians should remain in private practice "to serve as a pressure valve and standard of comparison." In his opinion, "Some taxpayers, though required to support the [National Health Service], will nevertheless want to pay private doctors for services that would be denied by Government physicians as unnecessary." He illustrates this by pointing out, "We'll always need doctors to do face-lifts, hair transplants, cosmetic breast surgery, hysterectomies in healthy young women, vasectomies, and circumcisions—elective procedures that taxpayers should never be asked to pay for." Dr. Bauer believes there are other reasons why fee practice should be dumped, like the extensive and costly bookkeeping of itemizing and billing for every drug, service, and test provided by doctors and hospitals. He argues that the "discontinuance of patient billing and maintenance of accounts will result in astronomical savings in medical office and hospital overhead."

Many other laymen and physicians believe that the overall effect of fee-for-service medical practice is deleterious on the quality of care. For example, Dr. George Crile, Jr., argues that incentive fees have a bad effect in the practice of law—especially in the area of medical malpractice. He points out that the United States is the only country under English law that legally allows lawyers to take part of a settlement as a contingency fee. United States medical malpractice lawyers often get up to 50 percent of a medical malpractice settlement. Their fee is contingent on winning the case. But in England such a practice is called barratry, is illegal, and is punishable by a fine or suspension from the bar. He says it is no "coincidence that in this country, where barratry is tolerated, the cost of malpractice insurance is 30 times as high as in England." "Perhaps from the patient's point of view and from that of the congressional committee, fee-for-service surgery is viewed no more kindly than we as physicians view barratry. I suggest we abolish both of these evils as soon as possible," concludes Dr. Crile.

What does he propose as an alternative? "In order to avert the socialization of medicine," he calls for a "privately operated salaried system based on the hospital." He argues that all hospital-based physicians like surgeons, pathologists, and many radiologists should be salaried to avoid the conflicts of interest and fee-induced overutilization of medical services both possible and apparent in our fee system. Marcia Millman, in *The Unkindest Cut,* also contends, "Our health care system will not truly serve the needs and welfare of the public until it is separated from profitmaking enterprises."

Needless to say, there would be many problems in converting our fee-for-service system into a manageable and equitable system of salaried physicians. It could be done slowly by means of the growth of government-supported health maintenance organizations. It could be done partially by salarying hospital-based physicians as Dr. Crile suggested, or it could be done more completely by the creation of a National Health Service as Dr. Bauer has suggested.

I believe that action must be taken in both areas—that is, the improvement of a series of quality control mechanisms in hospitals and credentialing of physicians, as well as the institution of salaries for physicians.

When Senator Ted Kennedy asked Dr. Alex Gerber, a Los Angeles surgeon, why Swedish children had only one-tenth as many tonsillectomies as did indigent children in California, Gerber replied:

Because we have a double standard of medical care in this country. Because we have one group of patients who get the very best that the world has to offer and another group of patients who get probably some of the worst. And the reason is that we do not control the practice of medicine strictly enough in our hospitals.

Dr. Gerber then pointed out that many doctors who would be barred from operating in veterans' or well-regulated hospitals can "operate with impunity" in some of the small and unregulated hospitals in this country. Not only are there double standards in hospital care, says Gerber, there are double standards in who does surgery, from diplomates of the American Board of Surgery to "a doctor who has not had a single day of surgical training in his life beyond his internship" but who lists himself as a surgeon in the yellow pages of a phone directory.

We do have a free enterprise system of medical care that allows the medical profession to regulate itself quite freely. While it has some advantages, it has some drawbacks which result in some surplus surgery and some poor surgery. I believe we ought to have a system where patients do not have to be so wary about the selection of a surgeon, in ignorance of his credentials, his motivations, and his skills.

But until the time when that system arrives, I believe a smart patient ought to seek out more information about the physician who treats him. I believe he ought to ask him more questions—to make better use of his physician, if you will. And I believe many doctors, not all, would welcome more curious and questioning patients.

To combat personally the possibility of a questionable operation being performed, there are a number of things that you, as a potential candidate for surgery, might do. Avoid going directly to a surgeon for medical care unless you are 100 percent positive that you want or need the surgery. Trained in surgery, the surgeon is more likely to find it warranted than would other doctors. Your initial visit would be better served by going to an internist, a family doctor, or a general practitioner.

If your nonsurgeon believes you may need surgery and wants to refer you to a surgeon, you may want to question him further. Ask him for several names, not one. Ask him about the credentials and track records of these men or women. And ask him about whether he would consider them conservative or liberal in their interpretation of the need for surgery. Should you go to the one, you later may want to visit the second for another opinion in your case.

You should also determine if the surgeon you decide to visit or are referred to is certified by one of the boards such as orthopedics or general surgery or otolaryngology. While this does not automatically mean your doctor is competent or excellent, it does mean that he has special training in surgery, that he has passed a rigorous examination to test his surgical knowledge, and that he has had at least two years of experience as a surgeon. If you are willing to settle for less than a board-certified surgeon, at least try to find someone who has had a residency in some surgical specialty or general surgery. This is not to say that general practitioners who do surgery, especially minor surgery, do it poorly. But it is to say that the chances of getting good and only necessary surgery performed are probably best with the most qualified practitioners.

You may also want to determine if your surgeon is a fellow of the American College of Surgeons. To be a member of this organization one must be board-certified. The organization tries to emphasize continuing medical education and high standards for its members.

Should your surgeon recommend surgery, consider getting a second opinion from another surgeon, especially from one who is known as conservative in medical circles—if you can obtain this information. This may be particularly important where the surgery is elective and one of those frequently cited as being overutilized—tonsillectomies, hysterectomies, hemorrhoidectomies, gallbladder surgery, lower back surgery, and more recently coronary bypass surgery. Many insurance companies are now covering the cost of second opinions in elective surgery. Even if the cost of a second opinion is not covered, the possible financial savings and the suffering and risks averted may well be worth the cost of paying it out of your pocket.

"As long as Americans entrust their health to doctors, they'll pay more and more for less and less," says Dr. John H. Knowles. When asked if patients should be skeptical about the advice they get from doctors, Knowles replied:

At the very least, a patient should ask—politely, of course, because he's at the mercy of his doctor—for a second opinion. This is especially true if the operation is at all dubious, such as surgery on the lower back for pain. This is a major area of excessive surgery. It's very serious to have your back operated on, and even when it is needed it's not always successful.

But Knowles contends that this is only one example. He says second opinions would be useful in hysterectomies, and "Another area is the tonsillectomy. Ninety-nine percent of them are unnecessary, yet we do anywhere from 800,000 to a million of them a year. Ridiculous. It costs billions."

When you choose a doctor, you often choose a hospital too. Most surgeons usually have privileges to do operations at only a few hospitals. But if you have a choice, pick a hospital that is accredited by the Joint Commission on Accreditation of Hospitals. This certainly does not ensure that it will be currently living up to all the accreditation standards, but it may help improve the chances that it is a well-run institution. Ask if the hospital has a peer review process that involves tissue audits and utilization reviews. It if does, and these are well done, it may improve your chances for high quality care.

Teaching hospitals often have better track records in survival rates and fewer complications following surgery. Yet, because there are more doctors—interns and residents—around most of the time in such hospitals (helpful in case of emergency complications), some of the care in such institutions is seen as more impersonal. In such places you may be subjected to more tests, prodding, and interviews so the residents and interns can learn from it. If you do not mind such multiple scrutinies, it may be worth it to have several medical minds rather than one working on your "case." Generally, some of the best-trained surgeons using the most up-to-date knowledge and techniques will be found at teaching hospitals. If you have the choice, especially if undergoing complicated surgery, a teaching hospital affiliated with a medical school is a good choice.

If the option is available, you may want to consider joining a prepaid group plan where the doctors are salaried and consultation is usually easily available. With an emphasis on preventive rather than curative medicine and no physician conflicts of interest between appropriate care and fees, such health maintenance organizations, with a few exceptions, have established an excellent record of minimizing questionable surgery and hospital stays. Or choosing a surgeon who participates in a multi-group fee practice where consultation with nonsurgical specialists is convenient may be beneficial to you.

A smart patient is one who is sufficiently concerned about his own condition that he wants to participate in making the decisions about it. Of course, many patients are not in the physical or mental condition to be informed decision makers when they are ill. Often they must rely on the help and advice of relatives, friends, and doctors. But insofar as they can, they or their families should ask questions. They should ask the referring doctor and the surgeon about the alternatives to surgery. They should ask about the possible benefits, negative side effects, complications, and risks associated with both medical and surgical alternatives. They should frankly ask not only about fees but also the track record of the surgeon who will be doing the surgery. While this may seem to suggest an abrasive questioning of the surgeon, it need not be done that way. The patient should recognize that it is his life and health at stake, not that of the surgeon whose services he is paying for.

It may seem strange to say, but do not push for surgery. When patients are in pain or depressed, they sometimes rather irrationally think that "someone or something has to help me." They may be grabbing at straws.

Often surgery is magnificently helpful; but sometimes it isn't. It may leave the patient in the same or worse condition despite the suffering and cost of an operation. There may be relief or cure for the condition, but it may not be in surgery.

In the same vein, in choosing a surgeon one should not necessarily choose the busiest one or the one with the best bedside manner. While the humane quality of a surgeon may be important in giving confidence to a patient during a difficult time, more is needed. A patient needs a surgeon who both is skillful and exhibits good judgment in managing a case. He is one who recognizes his own limitations. He is one with a good track record—a doctor's doctor whose overall competence is excellent. He may not be the busiest surgeon in town, but he has time for his patients. You should avoid a surgeon who does not do enough surgery or enough of the particular type of operation you may need to keep his skills sharply honed.

And before the operation proceeds and you give your final consent to it, ask who will be doing it. This is especially important in a teaching hospital. It may be a ghost surgeon—usually a resident. Many residents, fledgling surgeons, are excellent. But you have the right to determine whose hands your care will be in. You may not mind that a resident does part or assists in the surgery. You may not mind if he does all of it, either under the supervision of your surgeon or not. But since it is you who are having this elective surgery, it is also your right to determine who shall do it.

And of course it does not hurt to ask many other questions while you are in the hospital. You may ask about the nature of preparations and medications and tests before surgery or after it. Since errors are made in hospitals, some of which are damaging to patients, you may want to question if you have the right medicine or if you are the right person for a particular diagnostic test.

As Dr. Seymour Isenberg and Dr. L. M. Elting write in *The Consumer's Guide to Successful Surgery*, "The time is past when the surgeon can impose his favorite treatment on a patient by the strength of his will or the awe in which he is held. Some patients still permit it to happen because it's easier to have the surgeon do their thinking for them, or they are too frightened of him to think of saying no to his decision." Then they point out that there are "various possibilities for most operations" and that "only after alternative methods of treatment are discussed is your decision to be made and the consent form for a specific procedure signed."

At some time you may want to see your hospital records. While you have paid for them, they do not belong to you. They belong to the hospital. Surprisingly, in only nine states can a patient or his attorney see his medical records without instituting a lawsuit against the hospital or doctor and having the records subpoenaed for evidence. You may get around it by threatening to sue the hospital if it will not let you see your records. As a patient you have a number of rights—the right to medical care, privacy in your person, confidentiality in your records, and the right to consent or to withhold that consent for any procedure in light of the information given to you. You have the right to choose your physician and to be informed about what he is doing to you or plans to do. And, in the words of Dr. Marvin Belsky, "If you leave your doctor, you have a right to have your records sent to a doctor of your choice." I believe patients need to be more fully aware of their rights as patients and to assert them when they are not automatically given.

I would like to end this book on a positive note. In writing about the lack of regulation of American surgery which results in some which is unnecessary or of poor quality or both, the reader may think I am against all surgery or surgeons. Far from it. Most surgical procedures undertaken in the United States are well done and either necessary (in the sense of prolonging life) or desirable (in the sense of enhancing the quality of life). The SOSSUS report estimates that money spent on surgical research is well spent. For every dollar spent on sixteen major surgical research advances, there is a return anywhere from $60 to $135 in reduced mortality and morbidity. The variation depends on how one counts expenditures for research. But both research and the practice of surgery need to be better regulated. And we need to eliminate the conflict of interests surgeons have in our fee system so that the welfare of patients is paramount.

NOTES

PREFACE

Page

ix Statistics and reasons for rising number of hysterectomies: Ronald Kotulak, "Rising Hysterectomy Rate Comes under Scrutiny," *Boston Globe,* June 29, 1976, p. 21.

x Statement by Dr. Berman: Ronald Kotulak, "Are Doctors Ripping Us Off?" *Boston Globe,* Feb. 13, 1977, p. A3.

1: TOO MUCH SURGERY?

3 Unnecessary surgeries, deaths: "Cost and Quality of Health Care: Unnecessary Surgery," Report by the Subcommittee on Oversight and Investigations of the Committee on Interstate and Foreign Commerce, Ninety-Fourth Congress, 2nd Session (Washington: U. S. Government Printing Office, 1976).

3 Rita J. Nickerson et al., "Doctors Who Perform Operations" (Part 1), *New England Journal of Medicine* 295 (Oct. 21, 1976): 921–26.

3 Eugene G. McCarthy and Geraldine W. Widmer, "Effects of Screening by Consultants on Recommended Elective Surgical Procedures," *New England Journal of Medicine* 291 (Dec. 19, 1974): 1331–35.

3 Richard Cabot quoted by Lloyd Shearer in "Unnecessary Surgery," *Parade,* Sept. 7, 1975, p. 7.

3 Ivan Illich, *Medical Nemesis* (New York: Random House, 1976), pp. 28, 112.

3-4 Statistics on surgery: U. S. Dept. of Health, Education, and Welfare, *Surgical Operations in Short-Stay Hospitals: United States–1973,* May, 1976; and Darryl D. Enos and Paul Sultan, *The Sociology of Health Care* (New York: Praeger, 1977), p. 351.

5-6 AMA response (Sammons): "House Panel Report on Unnecessary Surgery Assailed by AMA," *New York Times,* Feb. 10, 1976, p. 27; William E. Farrell, "AMA Scores 'Unneeded Surgery' Report," *New York Times,* May 12, 1976, p. 48.

6-7   Statements by Dr. McCarthy, "Effects of Screening," 1331–34.

7   Statistics on unnecessary surgery, costs, and mortality: subcommittee report.

8   UMW-Klaw quotation: Spencer Klaw, *The Great American Medicine Show* (New York: Viking, 1975).

9   Ralph Emerson and John Creedon quoted in "Use Present Criteria for Surgery, MDs Recommend," *American Medical News,* April 25, 1977, p. 18. Quotation and figures on low incidence of unnecessary surgery in Ralph Emerson, "Unjustified Surgery: Fact or Myth?" *New York State Journal of Medicine,* March, 1976, pp. 454–60.

9-10   Quotation from Dr. Sammons: "AMA Again Challenges Second-Opinion Proposal," *American Medical News,* May 16, 1977, pp. 1, 9.

10   Emerson, "Unjustified Surgery."

11   Press quotations from Drs. Hiatt, Bunker, Barnes: "Calm Voices Join 'Unnecessary Surgery' Debate," *American Medical News,* May 30, 1977, pp. 1, 9.

11-12   Clark C. Abt, "The Issue of Social Costs in Cost-Benefit Analysis of Surgery," in John P. Bunker, Benjamin A. Barnes, and Frederick Mosteller (eds.), *Costs, Risks, and Benefits of Surgery* (New York: Oxford, 1977).

12-13   Quality and quantity outcomes of surgery: "Calm Voices," pp. 1–9.

13   Quotation from Dr. Gerber: Letter to the editor, *New England Journal of Medicine* 291 (Sept. 19, 1974): 635.

2: CASE STUDIES

14   Woman with miscarriage: Angela R. Holder, "Unnecessary Surgery," *Journal of the American Medical Association* 232 (June 9, 1975): 1059–60.

15   William A. Nolen, *A Surgeon's World* (New York: Random House, 1972), p. 310.

15-16   Woman with hysterectomy and back pains: ibid. "Cost and Quality of Health Care: Unnecessary Surgery," Report by the Subcommittee on Oversight and Investigations of the Committee on Interstate and Foreign Commerce, House of Representatives, Ninety-Fourth Congress, 2nd Session (Washington: U. S. Government Printing Office, 1976).

16-17   Five tonsillectomies: ibid.

17   California tonsillectomy rate: Alex Gerber, *The Gerber Report* (New York: McKay, 1971).

17   Spleen operation: Holder.

17-18   Cervical sympathectomy: ibid.

18   Double mastectomy: ibid.

18-19   Gerber.

19   Twelve children with yersiniosis: "Surgery by Non-Surgeons," *New York Times,* Oct. 24, 1976, sec. 4, p. 6; "12 Have Appendectomies after Mistaken Diagnosis," *Boston Globe,* Oct. 12, 1976, p. 2.

19-20   Howard and Martha Lewis, *The Medical Offenders* (New York: Simon and Schuster, 1970).

20   Testimony of Dr. Bluestone: "Quality of Surgical Care: Vol. I," Hearings before the Subcommittee on Oversight and Investigations of the Committee on Interstate and Foreign Commerce, House of Representatives, Ninety-Fifth Congress, 1st Session (Washington, U. S. Government Printing Office, 1977).

21-22   Testimony of Bill Haines: ibid.

22-23   Marcia Millman, *The Unkindest Cut: Life in the Backrooms of Medicine* (New York: Morrow, 1977), pp. 138–39.

23-25 Richard A. Knox, "Doctor Accused of Unjustified Surgery," *Boston Globe,* April 11, 1976, pp. 1, 32, 33.
   25 Alan M. Gittelsohn and John Wennberg, "On the Incidence of Tonsillectomy and Other Common Surgical Procedures," in John P. Bunker, Benjamin A. Barnes, and Frederick Mosteller (eds.), *Costs, Risks, and Benefits of Surgery* (New York: Oxford, 1977).
26-28 Dr. Nork: Marsha L. Johns, "Court Decision Would Extend Liability," *Hospitals* 48 (Jan. 16, 1974): 31–34; Jay H. Hedgepeth, "But the Publicity Is Premature," *Hospitals* 48 (Jan. 16, 1974): 34, 103–7; Bart Sheridan, "Why the Lawyers Caught Nork and the Doctors Didn't," *Medical Economics,* July 22, 1974, pp. 91–109; "What You Haven't Read about the Nork Case," *Medical Economics,* July 22, 1974, pp. 39–90.

3: UNNECESSARY SURGERY?

30-31 Five categories of surgery: Robert E. Rothenberg, *The New Understanding Surgery: The Complete Surgical Guide* (New York: New American Library, 1974).
   32 Walter H. Greene, "The Search for a Meaningful Definition of Health," in Donald Read (ed.) *New Directions in Health Education* (New York: Macmillan, 1971).
   32 Quotation on unnecessary surgery: American College of Surgeons and American Surgical Association, *Surgery in the United States: A Summary Report of the Study on Surgical Services for the United States* (SOSSUS), 1975, p. 89.
32-35 Six categories taken from ibid. and "Cost and Quality of Health Care: Unnecessary Surgery," Report by the Subcommittee on Oversight and Investigations of the Committee on Interstate and Foreign Commerce, House of Representatives, Ninety-Fourth Congress, 2nd Session (Washington, U. S. Government Printing Office, 1976).
   35 Blue Shield and quotation by Dr. Hanlon: "Blue Shield Curbs Surgery," *American Medical News,* May 23, 1977, pp. 1, 8.
   36 Frances D. Moore editorial: "Contemporary American Surgery: Hard Data at Last," *New England Journal of Medicine* 295 (Oct. 21, 1976): 953–54.
36-39 Unnecessary and unjustifiable surgery: see William A. Nolen, *A Surgeon's World,* esp. chap. 31, "Unjustifiable Surgery."

4: SURGERY AS A PLACEBO

   42 Arthur K. Shapiro, "Semantics of the Placebo," *Psychological Quarterly* 42 (April, 1968): 653–95.
   42 Placebo relief: Henry K. Beecher, "The Powerful Placebo," *Journal of the American Medical Association* 159 (Dec. 24, 1955): 1602–6; F. J. Evans, "The Power of a Sugar Pill," *Psychology Today* 7 (April, 1974): 55–59.
43-45 Henry K. Beecher, "Surgery as Placebo: A Quantitative Study of Bias," *Journal of the American Medical Association* 176 (July 1, 1961): 1102–8.
   45 Quotation from S. Wolf found in Richard S. Ross, "Surgery for Coronary Artery Disease Placed in Perspective," *Bulletin of the New York Academy of Medicine* 48 (Oct. 1972): 1163–78.

45 L. A. Cobb et al., "Evaluation of Internal Mammary-Artery-Ligation by Double Blind Technic," *New England Journal of Medicine* 260 (May 28, 1959): 1115-18; E. G. Dimond et al., "Evaluation of Internal Mammary-Artery-Ligation and Sham Procedure in Angina Pectoris," *Circulation* 18 (Oct., 1958): 712-13; Beecher, "Surgery as Placebo."

46-47 Arthur K. Shapiro, "Etiologic Factors in Placebo Effect," *Journal of the American Medical Association* 178 (July 23, 1963): 713.

47 Beecher, "Surgery as Placebo."

48 William A. Nolen, *Surgeon under the Knife* (New York: Coward, McCann and Geoghegan, 1976), p. 49.

48-49 Tonsillectomy and tuberculosis studies: Eliot Freidson, *Profession of Medicine* (New York: Dodd, Mead, 1970), chap. 12.

49 Duane F. Stroman, *The Medical Establishment and Social Responsibility,* (Port Washington, New York: Kennikat, 1976).

50 Sissela Bok, "The Ethics of Giving Placebos," *Scientific American* 231 (Nov., 1974): 17-23.

51 Ethics of placebo use: Arthur K. Shapiro, "Attitudes toward the Use of Placebos in Treatment," *Journal of Nervous and Mental Disease* 130 (March, 1960), 200-211.

51 Arthur K. Shapiro and Elmer L. Struening, "A Comparison of the Attitudes of a Sample of Physicians about the Effectiveness of Their Treatment and the Treatment of Other Physicians," *Journal of Psychiatric Research* 10 (Oct., 1974): 217-24; also see Shapiro and Struening, "Defensiveness in the Definition of Placebo," *Comparative Psychiatry* 14 (Jan.-Feb., 1973): 107-20.

51-52 Robert P. Bolande, "Ritualistic Surgery: Circumcision and Tonsillectomy," *New England Journal of Medicine* 280 (March 13, 1969): 591-96; H. E. Evans, "Tonsillectomy and Adenoidectomy: Review of the Published Evidence for and against Tonsillectomies and Adenoidectomies," *Clinical Pediatrics* 7 (1968): 71-75.

52 F. J. Ingelfinger, "Health: A Matter of Statistics or Feeling?" *New England Journal of Medicine* 296 (Feb. 24, 1977): 448-49.

5: HOW MUCH UNNECESSARY SURGERY?

54-55 William A. Nolen, *The Making of a Surgeon* (New York: Random House, 1970).

56 William A. Nolen, *A Surgeon's World* (New York: Random House, 1972).

59 James C. Doyle, "Unnecessary Hysterectomies: Study of 6,248 Operations in Thirty Hospitals during 1948," *Journal of the American Medical Association* 151 (Jan. 31, 1953); 360-65.

59 Paul A. Lembcke, "Measuring the Quality of Medical Care through Vital Statistics on Hospital Service Areas: 1 Comparative Study of Appendectomy Rates," *American Journal of Public Health* 42 (March, 1952): 276-86.

59-60 "Address of Dr. Henry V. Weinert," *Journal of the American Medical Association* 154 (Feb. 6, 1954): 521.

60 Paul A. Lembcke, "Is This Operation Necessary?" *New Republic* 149 (Nov. 9, 1963): 15-16.

60 Robert S. Myers and George W. Stephenson, "Evaluation for Tissue Committees," *Journal of the American Medical Association* 156 (Dec. 25, 1954): 1579.

60 Paul A. Lembcke, "Medical Auditing by Scientific Methods," *Journal of the American Medical Association* 162 (Oct. 13, 1956): 646-55.

61 Hawley information: Marguerite Clark and Karen Salisbury, "Operations—Needed and Not," *Newsweek* 50 (Aug. 5, 1957): 90, 92.

61 Martin Gross, *The Doctors* (New York: Random House, 1966).
62-63 Cromwell case: Howard and Martha Lewis, *The Medical Offenders* (New York: Simon and Schuster, 1970).

6: MORE EVIDENCE: Search for Causes

65-67 Charles E. Lewis, "Variations in the Incidence of Surgery," *New England Journal of Medicine* 281 (Oct. 16, 1969): 880–84.
67-68 John Wennberg and Alan Gittelsohn, "Small Area Variations in Health Care Delivery," *Science* 182 (Dec. 14, 1973): 1102–8.
68-69 John P. Bunker, "Surgical Manpower: A Comparison of Operations and Surgeons in the United States and in England and Wales," *New England Journal of Medicine* 282 (Jan. 15, 1970): 135–43.
69 Francis D. Moore editorial, "What Puts the Surge in Surgery?" *New England Journal of Medicine* 282 (Jan. 15, 1970): 162–64.
70-71 Eugene Vayda, "A Comparison of Surgical Rates in Canada and in England and Wales," *New England Journal of Medicine* 289 (Dec. 6, 1973): 1224–29.
71 John P. Bunker and John Wennberg, "Operation Rates, Mortality Statistics and the Quality of Life," *New England Journal of Medicine* 289 (Dec. 6, 1973): 1249–51.
73-74 George S. Perrott, "Utilization of Hospital Services," *American Journal of Public Health* 56 (Jan., 1966): 57–64.
74 J. E. F. Hastings et al., "An Interim Report on the Sault Sainte Marie Study: A Comparison of Personal Health Services Utilization," *Canadian Journal of Public Health* 61 (July/Aug., 1972): 289–96.
74-75 Duane F. Stroman, *The Medical Establishment and Social Responsibility* (Port Washington, N. Y.: Kennikat, 1976).
75-76 Donald C. Riedel et al., *Federal Employees Health Benefits Program: Utilization Study* (Rockville, Md.: U. S. Department of Health, Education, and Welfare, 1975).
76-77 Gerald T. Perkoff et al., "Lack of Effect of an Experimental Prepaid Group Practice on Utilization of Surgical Care," *Surgery* 77 (May, 1975): 619–23.
77 Paul A. Lembcke, "Is This Operation Necessary?" *New Republic* 149 (Nov. 9, 1963): 15–16.
77 Mary Goss, "Organization Goals and Quality of Medical Care," *Journal of Health and Social Behavior* 11 (Dec., 1970): 255–68.

7: MORE EVIDENCE: Second Opinions

79-81 Eugene G. McCarthy and Geraldine W. Widmer, "Effects of Screening by Consultants on Recommended Elective Surgical Procedures," *New England Journal of Medicine* 291 (Dec. 19, 1974): 1331–35.
81-82 Quotations from Emerson and Stahl in Frances Cerra, "Program Here Finds 28% of Surgery Unnecessary," *New York Times*, Dec. 15, 1974, p. 1.
82 Mineworkers: John P. Bunker, "Surgical Manpower: A Comparison of Operations and Surgeons in the United States and in England and Wales," *New England Journal of Medicine* 282 (June 15, 1970): 135–143.
82-83 Sammons and McCarthy quotations from Jane E. Brody, "Cornell Study Finds 11% of Surgery Is Unnecessary," *New York Times*, May 3, 1976, p. 62.

83 Mary Barber: "Cost and Quality of Health Care: Unnecessary Surgery," Report by the Subcommittee on Oversight and Investigations of the Committee on Interstate and Foreign Commerce, House of Representatives, Ninety-Fourth Congress, 2nd Session (Washington: U. S. Government Printing Office, 1976).

83-84 Hysterectomies, and quotation from Sammons: "AMA Official Defends Most Hysterectomies," *Boston Globe,* May 3, 1977, p. 2.

84-85 Cost-benefit analysis of hysterectomies: John Bunker, Klim McPherson, and Philip Henneman, "Elective Hysterectomy," in John P. Bunker, Benjamin A. Barnes, and Frederick Mosteller, *Costs, Risks, and Benefits of Surgery* (New York: Oxford University Press, 1977).

85-86 "Cost and Quality of Health Care."

86-87 Quotations from Mahoney, Blackman and New York Trial Lawyers Association in C. Gerald Fraser, "Trial Lawyers Score 'Unneeded' Surgery," *New York Times,* March 27, 1977, p. 31.

87-88 Medicaid regulations, AMA, and Donald Rubin statement in David Bird, "Hospitals in New York City Balk at Drive on Unneeded Surgery," *New York Times,* May 10, 1976, p. 40.

88 Judge George Pratt ruling in Max H. Siegel, "Medicaid Curb on Surgery Aid Upset by Court," *New York Times,* Jan. 20, 1977, p. 28.

89 Mass. Medicaid: Richard A. Knox, "Medical Aid Admission Check in Use Despite Court Order," *Boston Globe,* July 16, 1975, p. 4.

89 Operations denied under Medicaid in Massachusetts: "Another Crackdown on Unnecessary Surgery," *Medical Economics,* July 25, 1977, p. 12.

89 Reduction in Massachusetts surgery: "New Medicaid Rule Today: Second Look before Surgery," *Boston Globe,* March 1, 1977, p. 3.

89-90 Frances Cerra, "Before Surgery, 2nd Opinion Urged," *New York Times,* August 6, 1975, p. 28.

90 Max Parrott quotation from Jane E. Brody, "Blue Cross Acts to Limit Surgery," *New York Times,* March 16, 1976, p. 1.

90-91 Commercial insurance second opinions: James F. Smith, "Health Plans Allow Second Opinion," *Boston Globe,* Nov. 25, 1976, p. 52.

91 Reduction in New York Blue Cross surgery: "Need for Surgery under Scrutiny," *Pittsburgh Post-Gazette,* Feb. 27, 1978, p. 18.

8: QUALITY OF SURGERY

92 Francis D. Moore editorial: "What Puts the Surge in Surgery?" *New England Journal of Medicine* 282 (Jan. 15, 1970): 162–64.

92 William A. Nolen, *The Making of a Surgeon* (New York: Random House, 1970), p. 137.

92 Calvin B. Ernst, "Surgery, the Abused Word," *Surgery, Gynecology, and Obstetrics* 140 (April, 1975): 608.

92-93 Nurses' opinions in *Nursing:* "How Nurses Rate Hospital Care," *Time,* Jan. 17, 1977, p. 73.

93 "Ann Landers Answers Your Problems," syndicated column, Sept. 23, 1976.

94-97 William A. Nolen, *Surgeon under the Knife* (New York: Coward, McCann and Geoghegan, 1976), pp. 65, 55-56, 38-64.

97 Critical incident study: "U. S. Doctors: About 5 Percent Are Unfit," *New York Times,* Feb. 1, 1976, sec. 4, p. 11.

97-99 Cases and statistics: Jane E. Brody, "Incompetent Surgery Is Found Not Isolated," *New York Times,* Jan. 27, 1976, pp. 1, 24.

99-100 Anesthesia deaths and errors: Jane E. Brody, "Anesthesia Errors Linked to Deaths," *New York Times,* Dec. 16, 1976, p. 30.

100 Improper prescription habits, and studies: Boyce Rensberger, "Thousands a Year Killed by Faulty Prescriptions," *New York Times,* Jan. 28, 1976, p. 1.

101 Cancelation of ads in *Modern Medicine:* Martin Arnold, "Drug Ads Dropped over *Times* Series," *New York Times,* Feb. 10, 1976, p. 27.

101-102 Gerber quotations on GPs doing surgery: Alex Gerber, *The Gerber Report* (New York: McKay, 1971).

102-103 William A. Nolen, *A Surgeon's World* (New York: Random House, 1972).

104 Quotation from Dr. Robert Derbyshire found in Boyce Rensberger, "Few Doctors Ever Report Colleagues' Incompetence," *New York Times,* Jan. 29, 1976, p. 1.

104-105 Robert C. Derbyshire, "Medical Ethics and Discipline," *Journal of the American Medical Association* 228 (April 1, 1974): 59–62.

105 Gallbladder deaths reported by Derbyshire: Rensberger, "Few Doctors," p. 24.

105-106 Medical Conduct Board, Consumer Protection Board, and Peck quotations: Richard L. Peck, "Why People Feel Bad Apples Are beyond the Law," *Medical Economics,* July 25, 1977, pp. 119–24; "Misconduct Reporting Supported in New York," *American Medical News* May 30, 1977, p. 3.

106-107 Continuing medical education: John B. Gramlick, "Lifelong Learning: A Look at Continuing Surgical Education," *American Journal of Surgery* 132 (Dec., 1976): 683–87.

107-108 Variations in surgical outcomes by hospital: Staff of the Stanford Center for Health Care Research, "Comparisons of Hospitals with Regard to Outcomes of Surgery," *Health Services Research* 11 (summer, 1976): 112–27; Jane E. Brody, "Study Finds Danger in Surgery Varies Greatly among Hospitals," *New York Times,* Dec. 15, 1976, p. 1.

109 Random survey of accredited hospitals: Frances Cerra, "Surveys Uncover Hospital Hazards," *New York Times,* May 26, 1976, p. 30.

109 JCAH auditing: Jane E. Brody, "Audits Reducing Shortcomings of Hospitals," *New York Times,* Jan. 29, 1976, p. 24.

110 Saskatchewan hysterectomies: Frank J. Dyck et al., "Effect of Surveillance on the Number of Hysterectomies in the Province of Saskatchewan," *New England Journal of Medicine* 296 (1977): 1326–28.

111 Nolen, *A Surgeon's World.*

111-12 Doctor X's "See No Evil," March, 1976, *Quality Review Bulletin,* is reprinted in "Quality of Surgical Care: Vol. I," Hearings before the Subcommittee on Oversight and Investigations of the Committee on Interstate and Foreign Commerce, House of Representatives, Ninety-Fifth Congress, 1st Session (Washington, U. S. Government Printing Office, 1977).

9: TOO MANY SURGEONS?

113 Erwin A. Blackstone, "Misallocation of Medical Resources: The Problem of Excessive Surgery," *Public Policy* 22 (summer, 1974): 329–52.

113 Bornmeier quotation found in ibid.

113 James D. Hardy, "American Surgery–1976," *Annals of Surgery* 184 (Sept., 1976): 245–52.

113 George A. Zuidema, "SOSSUS and the Outlook for American Surgery," *Annals of Surgery* 182 (Oct. 4, 1975): 531–37.

114 William A. Nolen, *The Making of a Surgeon* (New York: Random House, 1970), p. 200.

114 Alex Gerber, *The Gerber Report* (New York: McKay, 1971), pp. 140, 144.

114-15   Hardy, "American Surgery."
115   Failure rates of foreign graduates: Zuidema.
116-17   For a discussion of the weighting system of the California Relative Value
         Index, see Rita J. Nickerson et al., "Doctors Who Perform Operations"
         (Part 1), *New England Journal of Medicine* 295 (Oct. 21, 1976): 921–26.
117-20   Discussion of surgical workloads drawn from ibid., part 2, 982–89, and
         the SOSSUS report: American College of Surgeons and American Surgical
         Association, *Surgery in the United States: A Summary Report of the
         Study on Surgical Services for the United States* (SOSSUS), 1975; and
         Walter W. Houck, "Surgeons in the United States: Activities, Output,
         Income," *Journal of the American Medical Association* 236 (Oct. 18,
         1976): 1864–71.
120-21   F. X. Edward Hughes et al., "Time Utilization of a Population of General
         Surgeons in Community Practice," *Surgery* 72 (March, 1975): 371–83;
         Hughes et al., "Operative Workloads in One Hospital's General Surgical
         Residency Program," *New England Journal of Medicine* 284 (1973):
         660; Hughes, "Surgical Workloads in a Community Practice," *Surgery*
         71 (1972): 315; Hughes et al., "Utilization of Surgical Manpower in a
         Prepaid Group Practice," *New England Journal of Medicine* 291 (Oct. 10,
         1974): 759–63.
121   Responses of surgeons: John A. Siegel et al., "Questionnaire on Surgical
         Manpower and Residency Training," *Surgery* 80 (Aug., 1976): 277–82.

10: SURGICAL FEES

123   William A. Nolen, *A Surgeon's World* (New York: Random House, 1972),
         p. 193.
123-24   Health Research Group report: Richard D. Lyons, "Wide Variance Found
         in Fees for Surgery," *New York Times,* Feb. 18, 1977, p. 1.
124   "The Flying Gall Bladder," *New York Times,* March 1, 1977, p. 30.
124-25   Incomes of doctors: Arthur Owens, "Earnings Survey: Which Specialties
         Are Staying ahead of Inflation," *Medical Economics* Oct. 18, 1976,
         pp. 146ff.
125   Quotation from Dr. Berman found in Ronald Kotulak, "Are Doctors
         Ripping Us Off?" *Boston Globe,* Feb. 13, 1977, p. A3.
125   Surgeons' high fees: See Erwin A. Blackstone, "Misallocation of Medical
         Resources: The Problem of Excessive Surgery," *Public Policy* 22 (summer,
         1974): 329–52.
125   "Every specialty . . .": found in Kotulak.
126-27   On doctors' fees and insurance, see Spencer Klaw, *The Great American
         Medicine Show* (New York: Viking, 1975).
127-28   Marcia Millman, *The Unkindest Cut: Life in the Backrooms of Medicine*
         (New York: Morrow, 1977), p. 60.
128   Fee splitting unethical: American College of Surgeons, "Statement of
         Principles," *Bulletin of the American College of Surgeons,* Jan., 1975.
129   Dr. Hawley and AMA on fee splitting: William Michelfelder, *It's Cheaper
         to Die* (Derby, Conn.: Monarch Books, 1960), p. 77.
129-31   Nolen experience on itinerant surgery and fee splitting: *A Surgeon's
         World,* chaps. 20, 21, and p. 103.
132   "Nancy Cameron" case found in Toby Cohen and Marshall Levin, "Ghost
         Surgery," *Today—Philadelphia Inquirer,* June 6, 1976, pp. 38–44.
133   Surgery on relief recipients: Jonathan Fuerbringer, "Welfare Chief Suggests
         Surgery Done for Practice," *Boston Globe,* July 15, 1975, p. 1.
133-34   Statements of doctors on ghost surgery: see Cohen and Levin.

135   William A. Nolen, *The Making of a Surgeon* (New York: Random House, 1970), p. 50.
135-36   Statement by Dr. Berman in Kotulak.
136   Nolen, *The Making of a Surgeon,* pp. 197, 198.
136-37   Paul A. Lembcke, "Is This Operation Necessary?" *New Republic* 149 (Nov. 9. 1963): 15-16.
137   Alfred W. Bauer, "It's Time to Dump Private Practice," *Medical Economics* July 25, 1977, pp. 67-71.
137   Donabedian opinion given in Boyce Rensberger, "Few Doctors Ever Report Colleagues' Incompetence," *New York Times,* Jan. 29, 1976, pp. 1, 24.
137   Donnell W. Boardman, "Annual Discourse: The Dollars and Sense of Medical Care and Health Services: Relation," *New England Journal of Medicine* 291 (Sept. 5, 1974): 497-502.

11: CHANGING PEOPLE

138   Edgar Berman, *The Solid Gold Stethoscope* (New York: Macmillan, 1976), p. 82.
138   For a discussion of plastic surgery see ibid., and John Marquis Converse (ed.), *Reconstructive Plastic Surgery* (Philadelphia: W. B. Saunders, 1965).
139   Statement by Dr. Franklin Ashley in "The Plastic Surgery Boom," *Newsweek* 89 (Jan., 24, 1977): 73-74.
139-40   Frances Cook Macgregor, *Transformation and Identity: The Face and Plastic Surgery* (New York: New York Times Book Co., 1974).
140-42   Case of Ingrid DeValery found ibid.
142   Definition of reconstructive surgery in Macgregor.
143-44   Blue Cross–Blue Shield coverage, and statement by Dr. Peter Mozden, in Loretta McLaughlin "Breast Implant Coverage Ending," *Boston Globe,* March 7, 1977, p. 1; McLaughlin, "Blue Cross Will Cover Breast Implants," *Boston Globe,* June 2, 1977, p. 1.
145   Case of Charlotte B. abstracted from Macgregor.
146-48   Transsexuals, and statements by doctors on sex change: Herbert Black, "Is the Psychiatrist More Important Than the Surgeon?" *New England* magazine section in *Boston Globe,* Feb. 6, 1977, pp. 19ff.

12: CORONARY ARTERY BYPASS SURGERY

149   Marcia Millman, *The Unkindest Cut: Life in the Backrooms of Medicine* (New York: Morrow, 1977), p. 231.
149   William A. Nolen, *Surgeon under the Knife* (New York: Coward, McCann and Geoghegan, 1976), p. 153.
149   Milton C. Weinstein, Joseph Pliskin, and William B. Stason, "Coronary Artery Bypass Surgery: Decision and Policy Analysis," in John P. Bunker, Benjamin A. Barnes, and Frederick Mosteller, *Costs, Risks, and Benefits of Surgery* (New York: Oxford, 1977), p. 363.
149-50   For a discussion of the nature of this surgery and some statistics on it, see Nolen.
151   In discussing coronary bypass surgery I have relied heavily on the appendix "Coronary Artery Bypass Surgery: Laissez-Faire in American Surgical Experiments" in Millman.
155   Quotation from Dr. Barnard found in Donald Robinson, "What's Right and Wrong in Heart Disease Treatment," *Parade,* May 15, 1977, pp. 28-30.

155-58 Discussion of coronary artery bypass surgery at Malden and Mt. Auburn hospitals and in Arizona found in Richard A. Knox, "Heart Surgery Death Rate Probed at Malden Hospital," *Boston Globe,* Feb. 23, 1976, pp. 1, 10; Knox, "Experts to Review Malden Open Heart Surgery," *Boston Globe,* March 16, 1976, p. 10; Knox, "Hospital Says Heart Group Halted Surgery," *Boston Globe,* April 17, 1976, p. 1.

156 Surgical record of Dr. Richard Mamiya cited in "New Freeways for the Heart," *Time,* May 9, 1977, pp. 55–56.

157 Malden report of the American Association for Thoracic Surgery contained in "Quality of Surgical Care: Vol. I," Hearings before the Subcommittee on Oversight and Investigations of the Committee on Interstate and Foreign Commerce, House of Representatives, Ninety-Fifth Congress, 1st Session (Washington: U. S. Government Printing Office, 1977).

158 Richard Knox, "8 Heart Surgeons Face Quiz," *Boston Globe,* Oct. 30, 1977, p. 34.

159 Quotation from the "Report of the Intersociety Commission for Heart Disease Resources," found in "Optimal Resources for Cardiac Surgery: Guidelines for Program Planning and Evaluation," *Circulation* 52 (1975): A23–27.

159 Statement by Dr. Francis Moore, foreword in John C. Norman (ed.), *Cardiac Surgery* (New York: Appleton-Century-Crofts, 1972), p. xiii.

160 Quotation from anonymous surgeon found in Millman.

161 Quotation from Dr. Robert Replogle found in Donald Robinson, "What's Right and Wrong in Heart Disease Treatment," *Parade,* May 15, 1977, pp. 28–30.

13: POSTSCRIPT

163-66 William A. Nolen, *A Surgeon's World* (New York: Random House, 1972), pp. 156–159.

163-70 Marcia Millman, *The Unkindest Cut* (New York: Morrow, 1977).

166 Robin Cook, *The Year of the Intern* (New York: Harcourt Brace Jovanovich, 1972), p. 189.

170-71 Timothy L. Curran, "Old Surgeons Never Die—and That's the Problem," *Medical Economics,* July 25, 1977, pp. 67–71.

171-72 Alfred W. Bauer, "It's Time to Dump Private Practice," *Medical Economics,* July 25, 1977, pp. 67–71.

172-73 George Crile, Jr., "The Surgeon's Dilemma—Continued," *Archives of Surgery* 111 (Feb., 1976): 205.

173 Quotation from Dr. Alex Gerber found in Edward M. Kennedy, *In Critical Condition: The Crises in America's Health Care* (New York: Simon & Schuster, 1972), pp. 160–66.

175 Statement by Dr. John Knowles found in an edited transcript, John Van, "Dr. Knowles Has a Rx for Health Costs," *Boston Globe,* Aug. 5, 1977, p. 2.

177 Seymour Isenberg and L. M. Elting, *The Consumer's Guide to Successful Surgery* (New York: St. Martin's, 1976), p. 47.

178 For a discussion of patient rights, see George J. Annas, *The Rights of Hospital Patients* (New York: Avon Books, 1975); and Duane Stroman, *The Medical Establishment and Social Responsibility* (Port Washington, New York: Kennikat, 1976).

178 Marvin S. Belsky and Leonard Gross, *How to Choose and Use Your Doctor* (Greenwich, Conn.: Fawcett, 1975), p. 76.

178 SOSSUS report: American College of Surgeons and American Surgical Association, *Surgery in the United States: A Summary Report of the Study on Surgical Services for the United States* (SOSSUS), 1975.

INDEX

Abt, Clark, 11
Adenoidectomy, 20, 66
American Association for Thoracic
  Surgery, 157
American Board of Surgery, 107
American College of Surgeons, 12, 20,
  32, 35, 61, 128, 129, 130
American Medical Association, x, 5, 6,
  9, 61, 83, 87, 90, 104, 129
American Surgical Association, 32, 33
Anesthesia problems, 99
Angiogram, 150, 151
Appendectomies, 8, 19, 33, 59-60, 61,
  66, 73, 77
Arizona Board of Medical Examiners, 157
Ashley, Franklin, 139
Auditing, medical, 60, 110-111

Barnard, Christian, 155
Barnes, Benjamin, 10, 11
Bauer, Alfred, 137, 171-173
Beecher, H. K., 43, 45, 46, 47
Belsky, Marvin, 178
Berman, Edgar, 125, 135, 138
Biofeedback, 43
Blackman, Norman, 5, 86
Blackstone, Erwin, 113, 125
Blue Cross–Blue Shield, 8-9, 73-76,
  90-91, 143-144
Bluestone, Charles, 20
Boardman, Bonnell, 137
Bok, Sissela, 50
Bolande, Robert, 51-52
Bornmeier, Walter, 113

Boston Globe, 39
Brown, Robert, 56
Bunker, John, 10, 11, 12, 68-69

Cabot, Richard, 3
California relative value, 116-117
Cardin, Terry, 133
Carlson, Rick J., 161
Cerra, Francis, 90
Certified Hospital Admissions Monitoring
  Program, 24-25
Chicago Tribune, 21, 135
Cholecystectomies, 13, 66, 113
Clinical mentality of doctors, 49
Cobb, L. A., 45
Cohen, Toby, 134
College of Physicians and Surgeons of
  Saskatchewan, 110
Consumer's Guide to Successful
  Surgery, The, 177
Cook, Robin, 166
Coronary artery disease, 150
Coronary bypass surgery, viii, 149ff
Cosmetic surgery, 42-43, 138-140
Cost-benefit analysis of surgery, 10-13,
  84-85, 161
Costs, Risks and Benefits of Surgery, 11
Crile, George Jr., 172-173
Curran, Timothy, 170-171

Denenberg, Herbert, 159
Derbyshire, Robert, 104-105
Diethrich, Edward, 157
Dimond, E. G., 45